A GH

Hugh Scott has always been fascinated by ghosts and the supernatural. "I like spooky things," he says. "I grew up reading ghost stories, listening to them on the radio and I've had some creepy experiences of my own." It's no wonder then that he writes spine-chilling stories himself.

It was in 1984, two years after winning the Woman's Realm Children's Story Writing Competition that he decided to give up his job as an art teacher and become a full-time writer: "I had this feeling inside me, just sitting in my solar plexus – a little diamond of pure knowledge, very hard and strong, and I knew it wouldn't go away until I left teaching and became a writer." His first novel, *The Shaman's Stone,* was published in 1988 and several more titles soon followed. These include *Why Weeps the Brogan?* (Winner of the 1989 Whitbread Children's Novel Award), *The Haunted Sand, Something Watching, The Gargoyle, A Box of Tricks, The Place Between, The Camera Obscura, Freddie and the Enormouse,* and, most recently, *The Ghosts of Ravens Crag.*

Hugh Scott is married with two grown-up children and lives in Scotland.

Other books by the same author

A Box of Tricks

The Camera Obscura

Freddie and the Enormouse

The Gargoyle

The Haunted Sand

Something Watching

Why Weeps the Brogan?

For younger readers

Change the King!

The Summertime Santa

A GHOST WAITING

HUGH SCOTT

WALKER BOOKS
AND SUBSIDIARIES
LONDON • BOSTON • SYDNEY

First published 1993 by Walker Books Ltd
87 Vauxhall Walk, London SE11 5HJ

This edition published 1996

2 4 6 8 10 9 7 5 3 1

Printed in Great Britain

British Library Cataloguing in Publication Data
A catalogue record for this book is available
from the British Library.

ISBN 0-7445-5215-X

For Ron and Maggie,
straight from the loch!

1

Friday evening.
Andrew and Rosie visit the dead,
and meet something that even
Father can't explain.

"I'm sure it struck the church!" insisted Andrew.

He cupped his hands to the window. "It's so dark. Wow! More lightning! What a crash! The storm's moving away though. Switch off the light, Rosie. Listen to that rain!"

Rosie switched off the light. The glow of a table lamp shone from the landing into the bedroom. The curtains rustled. Andrew felt Rosie push beside him, her elbow on his head. He tried not to complain; not to remind her that he was nearly eleven and too tall really, to be leant on.

"It's like staring into a bottle of James's ink," said Rosie.

Andrew jerked from under her arm.

"Stop trying to be so poetic!" he said. "I'm going outside to look."

"Into the graveyard?" Rosie's voice trembled spookily. "With the lychgate light flickering in the rain, and dead people all squirmy-wormy!"

"Oh, shut up!" Andrew pinched Rosie's round

wrist, and she glimmered at him through narrowed eyes. Then she laughed.

"I'll take you," she said. "Wellingtons."

"I don't need taking!"

They ran down the stairs, Rosie jumping the last five steps, Andrew the last four. Then Andrew ran back up eight steps and touched the frame of a watercolour landscape, straightening it. To please James; to please his dead brother. The landscape was signed J. Ainsley, and heaved with hills. A stone circle stood very still, with clouds raging, and grass quivering around the stones.

Or so it seemed.

It was only paint.

Andrew dashed after Rosie. A wellington shot out from under the staircase. And another. He pulled them on.

Rosie backed from the cupboard, and pushed her feet into white wellies. Her arms burrowed into a green Hunter coat that had once belonged to James, and buttoned to the wrong side. She pulled on a woolly hat, making her yellow curls sit close about her cheeks.

"What are you staring at?" she demanded.

Andrew wasn't sure why he stared. James's coat perhaps. Though Rosie had worn it a thousand times. Or her curls; or her plump fingers tugging her hat straight. She was his sister. Sometimes he saw her as other boys might see her. A beautiful teenager.

"I *said*, what are you staring at?"

"Nothing. Where's my anorak? Thanks. Do you think Dad heard that lightning strike?"

"No chance!" Rosie reached for Andrew's throat and fastened his anorak high under his chin.

"Rosie! I can do that myself!"

"Father's working on a sermon. And Mother will be hiding in a cup of tea and a magazine."

"*Drinking* a cup of tea—"

"Hiding," insisted Rosie, and Andrew knew she was right. Rosie was usually right.

They ran along the kitchen passage.

Andrew struck the light switch that had LYCHGATE – SWITCH OFF printed beside it on a wrinkle of sticky tape. Father had put the tape there, to save Mother complaining about the light left on. Mother didn't like to look out from a back window and see the lychgate lit at night.

They pushed into the kitchen. Mother's blonde head was bent face-deep in a *Woman's Realm*. Her hand searched for the teapot.

"Told you!" cried Rosie.

"Hullo, dear," said Mother. "Told who what? You're not going out at this time? The meat should be on. And it's raining. I thought I heard thunder."

"Did you, Mum?" said Rosie innocently, and mouthed "hiding" at Andrew.

"We think the lightning knocked the church down," said Andrew, "and buried all the people in the graveyard."

"Oh, my goodness – !"

"He means the people who are already buried, Mum. Don't panic. And don't go phoning for ambulances."

"Oh, I wouldn't! Oh, you two! You're teasing me!" gasped Mother. "Be a dear, Rosalind, and plug in the kettle again. This weather is giving me the most dreadful head. You *will* be back to cook the stew? Are you really going to the graveyard? Oh."

Andrew watched his mother. The magazine flopped over her cup. Her hair bounced in folds too young for her face. She blinked vaguely at him, then prodded the magazine.

"I ought to be reading my *Moral Philosophy*. Of course," she sighed, "*you're* not afraid of anything." Her gaze wandered to the window where the graveyard waited in the darkness beside the back garden. "Don't..." Her mouth put on a smile.

Andrew knew that his mother didn't know what to say.

She tried to be like other mothers. But she didn't know how. And because she didn't know, Andrew and Rosie teased her. And loved her very much.

"We can only get wet," Andrew assured her.

"You could," Rosie told him, "fall into an open grave. He did that last year, Mum, and you thought he was at school camp for a week —"

"The kettle's boiling," said Andrew firmly. He glared at Rosie, and her cheeks turned pink. She hurried to rinse Mother's cup, and make the tea.

Andrew turned the handle of the back door.

He shook his head. He would say nothing about Rosie's blunder – fancy her mentioning an open grave!

Rosie buttoned James's coat up to her neck.

"Sorry," she whispered to Mother, then she hurried towards Andrew and followed him into the darkness which sprawled behind the house.

They strode, Andrew and Rosie, down the brick path, rain sparkling in the beam of Rosie's torch, the kitchen window behind them throwing a glow onto their cuffs.

Beside the brick path, trees crowded, keeping the garden and the graveyard apart.

Ahead of Andrew, an iron lamp post shone wetly on the roof of the lychgate. The lamp post was the lychgate light, lit by that switch in the house; and the lychgate, Andrew remembered, had not always been the entrance from the vicarage garden to the graveyard, but (before the vicarage existed) was the way-in for coffins, and the gate was a place to rest the lych – or corpse – during the first part of the burial service.

Andrew stood with Rosie under the gate's roof, listening to water pattering on its timbers. He let Rosie search the shadows for the latch.

"I smell burning," said Rosie. She swung the gate, and pointed the torch.

"Scorching," said Andrew. "I told you the lightning hit something."

The beam slithered across a gravestone.

"Go on," urged Andrew.

"It's creepy." Rosie hung back. "Watch out for holly leaves." She laughed. "Like fingernails catching."

"I'll go first," sighed Andrew. "Give me the torch. Mind this huge tomb. Why is it built like a box? What a noise the rain's making! Hear it gurgling in the drain? Ugh! That angel's wing is slimy! Rosie, I hope that's you touching my shoulder."

He led his sister carefully.

The rain made the darkness darker.

Andrew's feet crunched onto the gravel path which wound close around the church. He bounced the light on a window, then wobbled the beam higher. "There's one of your relatives!" he said.

A gargoyle scowled down from the gutter.

"Probably you!" gasped Rosie.

Andrew looked back through the rain towards the lychgate. Its light was a smear in the darkness. He turned, and saw distantly, beyond the front of the church, a street lamp glittering.

"Shine the torch around more!" hissed Rosie.

"Here's the tower—"

"Doesn't it look spooky in the wet!"

"The door's open. Dead leaves all up the stairs—"

"Close it! Oh, wait! I hear something. Shine the light that way."

Andrew turned from the door, leaving it open. He said, "James's grave is about there. It's too far to see. Hey, look at this!"

A trail of scorched grass led among the graves. Steam rose into the torchlight and, on the grass, darkness jumped behind fragments of stone.

"That stone's off the tower, Rosie! The lightning must have blasted it loose!"

Andrew swung the beam onto the tower wall, printing a shadow up beside the lightning conductor. On either side of the conductor, a copper-green stain had spread into the stonework. He couldn't see to the top.

He touched the conductor. It was warm.

"The lightning struck the conductor," he said, "then ploughed across the ground. Some stink."

"I never thought it would *travel*," whispered Rosie. "Let's see where it goes."

Her fingers pushed Andrew's spine, and he trod into the torch's bright puddle.

A yew tree leaned, tall as a house.

Something flapped.

"What's that on James's grave?"

Andrew thrust with the torch, as if pushing could pour more light through the rain.

He stepped forward, but Rosalind's hold on his shoulder jerked him behind the yew.

The thing on James's grave flapped again, like a newspaper in the wind.

"It's a newspaper," said Andrew. Drips rattled on the hood of his anorak.

He tugged free of his sister's fingers.

The paper jerked, dodging the torchlight, zigzagging away among the gravestones, vanishing into darkness.

Andrew frowned. Was it a newspaper? Or the owl that Father had seen?

Then lightning flickered, silently, brightening the graveyard into black and white.

Like one of James's drawings.

Rosie was whispering.

"What?" Andrew asked.

"James's stone is split!"

"What! Come on!"

Andrew ran.

The torchlight found the gravestone's polished surface.

Water crawled into the ragged shadow between the stone's two halves.

"Father won't be pleased!" gasped Andrew.

Rosie's face hovered in the gloom. She was staring behind him.

"That thing's coming back!" she breathed.

He turned.

Rosie's shriek pierced his ear.

"*I thought you said it was a newspaper!*"

Rosie's coat whirled as she fled.

Andrew wiped rain from his eyes.

The newspaper came toppling so swiftly that Andrew knew that running was sensible.

Throwing the torch wasn't sensible. But he threw it because it was in his hand. It slipped from his wet grasp and thudded near James's grave.

He heard the lychgate clank and Rosie's yelp, "Run!" so he ran, dodging gravestones.

He fled into the haze of light around the lychgate. Rosie hauled him through the gate, and he glanced back seeing the torch splashing a green fan across the grass; then something pale emerged from behind the box tomb.

He crashed the gate shut, and sped along the brick path, following his sister towards the bright kitchen window.

They hurtled into the kitchen and slammed the door.

Mother gaped. They thumped empty wellingtons onto the floor, dumping wet clothes, and shouting about what they had seen.

Then Rosie shared tea from Mother's teapot; and Andrew watched the magazine sag in Mother's grasp when she heard that James's stone was broken. Her fingertips went to her mouth.

She didn't really hear about the newspaper, but said, "Ask your father. He has an explanation for everything."

And Andrew – his thoughts muddling up James, the broken gravestone, and the rushing white thing – said too loudly, "Except James's death."

Mother's mouth drooped.

Rosalind dumped her tea down. "You little beast!"

"What?"

"How dare you say that!" Rosie jerked a glance at Mother.

"I only said —"

"I know what you said! Your head's so busy that you don't consider other people!"

"Rosie!" pleaded Andrew. "But *you* said earlier..." Andrew thought of reminding Rosie that she had joked about an open grave; then he looked at Mother and closed his mouth.

Rosie thudded away across the cold slate floor. The cutlery drawer crashed open.

Mother welcomed Andrew into her arms.

He watched Rosie thump a knife through carrots; she stung the air with onions.

Andrew sighed. He hadn't meant to hurt Rosie – or Mother. Sometimes he said what was true, and people were hurt. He would have to explain to Rosie what he had meant.

But later, when her temper was cool.

❧

Andrew stood in James's room.

It was becoming the spare room where books rose in piles, and black bags of laundry – neglected by Mother – leaned in uneasy slumber.

Drawing pins in the wallpaper marked the richer-coloured rectangles once hidden from daylight by James's posters.

Father's laughter rumbled from the hall below, filling the staircase with church-shaking volume.

"THE BARN OWL! HA! HA! NEVER THOUGHT MY ROSIE WOULD RUN FROM A BIRD! BET ANDREW WASN'T SCARED! I'LL BET YOU A CHOCOLATE BISCUIT HE'S OUT THERE BEFORE BEDTIME RETRIEVING THE TORCH! HA! HA!"

Andrew walked around the room looking at paintings and drawings in wooden frames. Each was signed J. Ainsley. Each sent shivers through Andrew; though James had drawn nothing gruesome – the posters had provided gruesomeness. James, really, at sixteen, had grown out of his teenage relish for blood and bones. Here was the softly painted town, here the thick brown church, energy in every twist of paint.

"Split?" Father's voice, subdued. "Lightning *struck* the stone?"

Andrew stared at the picture which repelled him most. It was really a map of the town, but with every building fiercely stroked-in with black ink. It showed the church and vicarage (where Andrew was now) at one end of the town, with Broad Street leading to the square; then Main Street beyond the square, all in a straight line.

A mile away, Main Street squeezed under the arch of the Bishop's Gate, which was once part of the ancient town wall. Beyond the arch, maybe another mile away, on a slight rise of grass, stood the stone circle. Andrew wasn't sure why he disliked this drawing. Perhaps because it made the town look haunted.

"Oh, it struck the lightning conductor." Father's voice filled the staircase. "What? Then travelled across the ground? Oh, I see. Oh, really! It's too bad! I wanted that drain replaced years ago! Yes, yes, Rosie. The same thing happened in the storm of eighty-seven. We lost two gravestones that time. There's an old iron drain apparently, close to where the conductor is earthed. The lightning follows the iron pipe. Oh, really!"

Andrew fingered the bookshelf. He touched volumes on magic, and made a face. How could James be so silly? His fingers passed along; he teased a book free. He flopped it open on James's drawing table.

The book lay flat as if used to being open at this page. On the page was a map, with a thick straight line printed across it.

Andrew compared the map with James's drawing of the town. They were the same, except the book version was simple, and the line across it ran from the church to the stone circle.

Under the map Andrew read:

The ley line in this area is remarkably strong. The author has tracked this ley by dowsing at different times of year. It is most active around the end of October.

Today was near the end of October.

Andrew tried to remember what "dowsing" meant.

And what was a ley line? How could a line be active? He might ask Father. He turned back a few pages.

A ley line is where ancient monuments, such as stone circles and churches, are in exact line with one another. Such a line (which may be a few miles, or several hundred miles long) appears to have energy that can be detected by dowsing. The energy readings are only reliable if made in a stone circle (or other point) where there has been no building and no interference from traffic.

Andrew didn't want to read this silly book. He shut it and saw the author's name.

John Maydick.

John Maydick had been James's friend. The one Mother called "young doctor John".

Andrew remembered a year ago, sitting in Father's study, stunned, after Doctor Maydick left, gripping Father's fingers, weeping, but relieved that James was dead.

Andrew walked round the drawing table to the window and pushed aside the curtain.

Raindrops ran on the glass. His reflection looked in from outside.

"Andrew."

"Oh! Hullo, Rosie. You made me jump."

"That's unusual." Rosalind perched, straight-backed on James's bed. Her eyes darted at Andrew.

Andrew gazed at James's bottle of drawing ink. Black dribbles hung thick on the bottle's neck. Andrew moved his head and saw a tiny reflection move in the black glass.

He sat on the bed, not too close to his sister. He heard Father's laugh drifting up from the sitting-room.

"I miss him," whispered Rosie. "Don't you miss him?" Her face accused Andrew. "Don't you have any *feelings!* How could you say that to Mother!"

Andrew tightened his lips.

"I only meant," he said gently, "that Father couldn't explain James's death. I wasn't trying to get at anyone."

"I suppose you forgot that Mother found James on the grass beside the lychgate!"

"Rosie—"

"He died of a heart attack! That's explanation enough! Father just couldn't accept it, that's all. Just as Mother still can't accept it."

"I'm sorry, Rosie."

Andrew returned to the window, hiding between the curtains and the glass.

Father had insisted that James's heart wasn't so weak that he would die without cause. After the funeral Mother burned her university books, and took to reading magazines.

Andrew said, "I think the rain's off."

"So what?"

He cupped his hands to the wet pane.

"We've got another torch, haven't we?"

Rain dripped from the lychgate roof.

Rosie raised the latch with hardly a click and they walked, not too quietly, noisily even, cheerfully even. "Ha!" said Rosie.

"Ha! what?" asked Andrew, and dazzled the torchlight on her face.

"Just, 'Ha'. I'm allowed to say, 'Ha' if I want."

"You're scared."

"I'm not. Here's the holly tree. You go first. Isn't it dark! We won't find anything."

"Do you think there's an owl?"

"No. Yes. Of course there is. Father's seen it. And we saw it—"

"You know what I mean," said Andrew. He pushed carefully between the holly and the box tomb. "Mind your face. The leaves are prickly."

"And wet!"

"It wasn't the owl. Mind your feet. This gravestone's slippy."

"I'm glad the rain's off. I see a star. Oh!" Rosie stumbled into the darkness.

Andrew pointed the torch down to find her. "Are you all right?"

She stood up holding her earthy palms to the light.

"I told you it was slippy," said Andrew.

"Get on!"

He walked, as Rosie pushed him forward.

"Don't push!"

"OK."

Push.

"Rosie!"

"What? Don't stop. Mind those branches."

"And don't you push!"

"I'm not."

Andrew's shoulder jerked from another thrust of Rosie's fingers. He tightened his lips.

"Nearly there," he said.

He stopped, braced for Rosie's *push*.

But she didn't push him, and he turned, wiggling the torch to find her.

But he was alone.

A car hummed on the distant road.

Something pale bobbed into the torchlight.

It was Rosie's face.

"I was washing my hands in the wet grass!" she said.

"You didn't push me?"

"Just the once."

"Well, something did."

"Branches," said Rosie. "Bobbing in the breeze." She stood close, the waxy smell of her Hunter flavouring the air. "Don't tell me you're scared? You're never scared, are you?"

"No. James used to push me."

"I don't mind going home."

"No!"

Andrew used the torch like an eye, letting the eye search for the white thing that might be an owl. Or a newspaper. He pointed the torch up into an elm, sliding the light along a naked branch.

Then they stepped on dead people, feeling their way around moss-soft stones.

"Here we are," said Rosie. "Poor James. The lightning's torn up the grave. Mother's flowers are all over the place. What a deep gash. It's horrid with the torchlight slipping into it. You don't think...?"

"What?"

"You know," she whispered.

"It can't be too deep," said Andrew. "Don't lean on me, Rosie. That is you leaning on me? I don't want to fall in." But he knew the gash was narrow.

"I suppose your arm might go down," said Rosie faintly. "Stretch in with the torch. Oh, don't dare! I didn't mean it! Haven't you any fear *at all!* What if..."

She giggled, her face close in the torch's glow. "What if someone reached up!" Her teeth gleamed, then she stood straight, her face in darkness, just the blank green of her coat in the torchlight.

Andrew said, "If anyone comes up, it will be James."

"Oh! Don't!"

Water trickled noisily.

"I see our other torch." Rosie stepped away and bent to the dark ground. She straightened, pressing at the torch with her thumb. "The rain must've got into it. Let's go home! Father will be upset at this gap in the earth. He wasn't happy when I told him James's stone was split. What are you waiting for?"

"The owl."

"Oh, that."

Andrew walked round the opened grave. Darkness stepped away from his torch. He felt empty space at his back.

He heard Rosalind's feet slithering in the grass.
She muttered, "It's only an old owl."

Andrew moved the torch, seeing stones leaning, stained with circles of lichen, and other stones, their polished faces shining because they were new. And black night lurked between trees where the light couldn't reach.

"What else could it be?" whispered Rosalind.

"What else could what be? Oh, the owl," sighed Andrew.

Suddenly, he wanted to weep.

He knew he wasn't scared, wandering here in the graveyard. He would have come alone to find the first torch, if Rosie hadn't volunteered. He would have come alone even to investigate the fluttering white thing. Andrew wasn't boasting to himself; he simply wasn't afraid; but how often – *how often!* had Rosie demanded answers to her questions! As if *he* knew everything that she didn't know!

A sob rose in his throat.

Rosie's feet strode close. He waited, letting her put her arms round him. Her cheek pressed his brow.

He breathed quickly, letting the sob fade.

Sometimes, Rosie was a mother to him.

"I forget you're so young," she said.

Andrew nodded inside her embrace. He didn't mind being called young. He would be eleven on his birthday. Young enough to appreciate his sister. But old enough to think for himself. And he was glad that she didn't ask what was wrong.

"Shall we go?" Rosie released him.

"I want to put the torch off for a minute. The owl might come."

"If you like."

He heard Rosie swallow. He switched off the torch, and they waited.

The darkness stood, almost solid.

Andrew breathed the scent of pine needles.

Was something moving?

He pointed the dark torch, ready to switch on.

He could see only blackness beneath the night sky.

"Now!" hissed Rosie.

He switched on.

Trees heaved as a breeze strode through the churchyard.

The pale thing rose into the torchlight.

It flapped towards Andrew and Rosie. Was it growing? Unfolding? It rushed and tumbled, quick as a child.

They ran; fleeing towards the iron lamp post, which flickered among the trees.

They staggered over humps on the ground. They ducked under branches.

They slammed through the lychgate, then Rosie shrieked; and Father's bulk, walking within a lit window in the house, turned to look out, then hurried away.

The back door opened. Mother stepped onto the path, hesitating.

Rosie fled to her.

Father billowed from the kitchen. "What's all this? Andrew? Is it a game? Rosie, was that you screaming? Are you hurt? Is someone there?"

Father half-strode into the garden's darkness,

but Andrew rushed into him and held him; then reached for Mother, shoving her, with Rosie, into the bright kitchen.

"Steady on!" growled Father, but Andrew snarled, and Father, startled, gathered his family through the doorway.

Andrew banged the door. He dragged Father to the window. "Put out the light!"

Rosie obeyed, and Andrew stared through the glass, Father at his side.

A star touched the sky.

Andrew scowled towards the graveyard until his eyes blotched. But he saw only branches around the glow of the lamp post.

He switched on the kitchen light.

"Oh, Andrew!" cried Mother. "Rosalind! What a fright! Are you really all right?"

"We're not all right!" said Andrew. "Rosie's crying."

"I didn't mean... Oh. As long as you're not hurt."

"Put the kettle on, Mary," said Father. "Now, you two. Coats off. Let me help with those wellies. It's time you were in bed. Sit at the table. Rosie, near the Rayburn. You're as white as my surplice." He polished Rosie's fingers between his large hands. "Is it a police matter?"

"Police?" whimpered Rosie.

"Was someone in the churchyard? Chasing you? Tell me quickly and I'll phone—"

"Oh! No. No one." Rosie's bewildered glance questioned Andrew.

"Nobody." Andrew met Mother's look as she

placed cups on the table.

Father relaxed into a chair, his eyes keen; on Andrew; on Rosie. He still held Rosie's fingers. Rain sprinkled on the window.

Everyone – thought Andrew – was listening for something outside.

Then the sweet smell of burnt raisins wakened Andrew's taste buds.

Mother served toasted teacakes. She dumped down butter.

The teacakes were scorched.

Father raised his eyebrows at Mother and stirred with an imaginary spoon. A spoon appeared. "Sugar, dear," said Father. "I've got a spoon. Well! Who's going to start? Andrew? Drink your tea, son. I do believe you're shivering. What's it all about? I know you saw an owl earlier, and it gave you a turn. Didn't I say, Mary, that he'd be off to find that torch? I'm glad you went with him." Father's hand patted Rosie's fingers.

"It wasn't an owl," said Andrew quietly.

Mother stared out from among her folds of hair. "*Sturm und drang*," she whispered, and Andrew stared.

He said: "It looked like a newspaper – at first."

Father's eyebrows rose.

"But..." Andrew's breath surged into his chest.

"Easy," murmured Father.

"You didn't see it! Toppling along. Coming to get us! It was taller than Mum!"

Andrew's breath rushed out in a sob. Father frowned and touched his shoulder.

Andrew thrust out of his chair and went to

Mother. She held him, teacake crunching as she chewed.

Father glanced towards the window. "I confess that I'm baffled. Coming fast, was it? There is a breeze? Taller than your mother? That's a little difficult to... Well... It must've been *something* to give Andrew a start." Father stood up.

"You can't go out!" gasped Andrew.

"I'll take God with me. Between us we'll get to the bottom of this." Father's eyebrows gathered into a bushy frown. "I won't have my children frightened," he said mildly.

Andrew arched his arm against the kitchen window. Torchlight splashed along the brick path, with Father's legs walking into it.

Rosie's chair scraped. Andrew leaned back from the window and watched her reflection huddle at the Rayburn. He saw also, her white wellingtons discarded on the floor, like little dead feet.

At the lychgate, the torchlight muddled among shadows. Then Father's bulk curved busily.

The torch glared at Andrew.

"He's coming back!"

"Already?" said Rosie.

"He didn't go through the gate." Andrew opened the outside door.

Light from the kitchen stretched down the garden. Father sang a pop song. Something pale waved from his grasp.

Andrew's heart bumped. Rosie stood beside him.

Father strode into the light. "Well!" he said. He came into the kitchen. Rosie and Andrew stepped away from the pale bundle dripping in his hand.

"Newspaper," said Father. "It was clinging to the far side of the lychgate." Father sounded puzzled. "There's not much breeze, really. And the paper was spread up the gate. Its pages are overlapping. Stand it up –" Father's eyebrows rose " – and it would be taller than your mother." He crushed the paper over the sink squeezing rainwater from it.

He hesitated.

Then he stuffed the paper into the pedal bin.

"Rosie, dear," said Mother as if nothing had happened, "I'm off to bed. You will wash the cups? Andrew, your hair's wet..."

"All right!"

Andrew glared at his father. He thundered up to the bathroom, and rubbed a towel over his hair.

He buried himself under his quilt.

2

Saturday morning.
Rosie and Andrew are polite to an old man,
and not so polite to a young one.

Cold sunlight filled Andrew's bedroom.

He heard Rosie singing. He dressed, being a ghost inside his pullover as he ran down to the kitchen.

Father stood at the Rayburn preaching to a frying pan floating with eggs and mushrooms.

"Is Mum out of bed?"

"Where's my hug?" demanded Father. "Thank you. Your mother has a headache."

"Doctor John said headaches shouldn't be ignored."

"Believe me," pronounced Father to the ceiling, "your mother is not ignoring her headache. Rosie has taken up tea and toast. I am the weekend cook. Eat well, and live with energy! Ah, Rosie. Sit in!" Father served.

They sat in, and silence sat with them.

Father's gaze roved to the pedal bin.

He paused often in eating, his head raised to contemplate the lychgate.

He said that the verger would attend to James's grave. Then, "One thing, children."

Andrew closed his mouth on mushrooms.

"That newspaper," said Father reluctantly, "was very wet. I rather think there wasn't enough breeze last night to blow it about."

Andrew frowned.

"But there must have been," said Rosie. "Newspaper can't tumble along if there's no wind. Maybe there was a gust. I don't remember now."

Her glance questioned Andrew, but Andrew sat with mushroom inside his cheek and recalled years ago, opening the cupboard under the stairs to find a figure with ghastly eyes, dropping onto him, then discovering it was James's jumper and jeans stuffed with *The Observer*, its printed head bound solid with string, and given a face made of James's paint.

He swallowed the mushroom. "Perhaps someone made it tumble along," he said.

"What do you mean?" Rosie stared at him, her eyes so blue that Andrew sat, startled.

He saw that she knew what he meant – that James had made the paper move.

But Andrew didn't want to say it in front of Father, so he ate up his mushrooms.

"Excuse me." Father got up. "Sermon to finish. Mother says will you do the shopping?"

Rosie shifted her gaze. "Oh. Right. And tidy the kitchen, I suppose. I *did* go up with her breakfast."

Father nodded. "You're good children." His strong face smiled. "God bless you," he said.

Sunlight sparkled, and trees in the drive at the front of the vicarage dripped last night's rain onto the earth.

Andrew unzipped the collar of his anorak, and Rosie marched beside him, her Hunter open, her hair snug under her woolly hat. She sang without words.

They left the drive, Andrew touching the wooden pillar that once supported a gate. He always touched the pillar for luck, but never said so. He was too adult to be superstitious.

Almost.

His fingers lingered on the timber as he passed the pillar. As his glance slid to his fingers, something moved in the drive behind him, and he turned, thinking Father had come after them. But the trees dripped, the earth glistened, and the vicarage sprawled in the sunlight.

"Come on, slowcoach."

Andrew trotted after Rosie, along the twist of pavement that put them in front of the church.

In the sunshine, the graveyard had no dark places; and its stones welcomed the daylight.

Andrew didn't mention the toppling newspaper. Rosie was singing, and he didn't want to spoil her good mood. She might buy him a cake.

Andrew wondered at his own childishness over cake. Everybody said he was so grown-up. "But I *am* a child!" he said out loud, and Rosie stopped singing.

"You're blushing!" she laughed. "And there's nothing wrong with being a child."

"I'd rather be grown-up."

"You're grown-up enough." She gazed towards the church.

Andrew looked. The gravestones stood still.

Rosie met Andrew's glance, her mouth soft. A smile curved her lips, then on! she strode, cheerful, down Broad Street with its wide pavements and shops in flat-faced buildings, and cherry trees in winter nakedness.

Andrew enjoyed walking through the town. Many of the buildings within the town wall were hundreds of years old and crookedly built of brick and oak. Some, even, were as old as the wall itself.

Beyond the wall lay the new town.

Even there, some buildings were ancient; but modern streets, designed for cars rather than people, spoiled it.

Andrew turned his head.

He had seen a movement, like someone dodging to stay out of sight behind him.

Had Father followed them? To remind them of something?

"I'm being stupid!" thought Andrew. "Father's writing a sermon! And he wouldn't dodge us! He'd be jollying us along, laughing!"

"It's too cold to dawdle!" said Rosie. "No one's following!"

Andrew ran at her. "Who says someone's following?"

Rosie's eyes glimmered blue, then she buttoned her Hunter and prodded her hair under her hat. "You were looking back," she said.

"So were you! You looked towards the church. Did you see someone?"

"No. Certainly not. Oh, silly! Who would follow us in broad daylight? Look! No one's paying any attention. I've a whole shopping list... Were you really not scared last night?"

Andrew glowered at the pavement.

"You're never scared," said Rosie. "Well, I was. But the breeze blew the newspaper. Must've done."

"Wet newspaper is heavy."

"Then we imagined it! Andrew, we were creeping among tombstones in the dark! And it certainly wasn't James who made the paper move, if that's what you think! I don't want to hear any more! And nobody's following us. We're nearly at the square. Take my hand crossing. Do what I say! Even grown-ups get run over!"

Andrew held Rosie's hand, and he was half ashamed and half glad. They crossed the road that circled the square.

He let go of her hand. They walked over the grass.

Andrew angled a glance up at the war memorial. The memorial placed a shadow, like a dark rag, across a bench.

Andrew looked back.

Cars hissed on the wet tarmac. People headed in every direction. Rosie was right. Nobody was paying any attention.

"*Hello.*"

"Oh!" Andrew reached for Rosie. He peered at the figure on the bench. Was it a woman? An old man?

"Goodness!" said Rosie. "Where did you spring from?"

Andrew stared, trying to see the person clearly,

but darkness seemed mixed up with the daylight. Had something gone wrong with his eyes? He saw Rosie perfectly, a frown cutting her brow.

"Hello," said Andrew. It was an old man. Of course it was. Andrew smiled.

"*Sun. Shining.*"

"Oh, yes!" said Rosie. "And not much rain. Wasn't it heavy last night?"

"*Long night. Heavy.*"

Andrew's neck prickled as if icy spiders walked on his skin. He stood facing the old man, but he was sure that if he turned he would find someone else at his back. He gazed at his own feet. He looked past his feet, turning slowly.

"I suppose it was a long night," agreed Rosie politely. "It's been nice talking to you. We're going shopping. Goodbye."

Andrew jumped round colliding with Rosie.

"Andrew!"

"Sorry."

There was no one behind him.

"Goodbye," said Rosie.

"'Bye," mumbled Andrew.

"*See you.*"

They walked on. "We'll go to the baker's first," said Rosie.

They crossed the road again (the road that circled the square) and entered Main Street.

A woman frowned at them, as if puzzled.

"Then the butcher's," said Rosie, eyeing the woman.

A child tugged its mother's hand and the mother gaped.

Andrew and Rosie raised their eyebrows. The child, dragged by its mother, stared.

"What are those two looking at?" demanded Andrew.

Rosie shrugged and led Andrew into the baker's.

The shop was empty. The girl assistant appeared and said, "Who's first?"

"We're together," said Rosie.

"I meant the young gentleman between you. Well! That's the strangest thing! I could've swore... Sorry, love. What can I get you?"

"Bread," said Rosie. "That crusty loaf, please..." She tilted her face at Andrew.

"*There's no one!*" he whispered.

"*I know!* Eight brown rolls, please. *Can you see anyone outside?*"

"*No! Rosie, I don't like this!*"

"We'll have a cake. What do you want?"

"A meringue."

"You'll mess your anorak. Two jam doughnuts, please."

"Jam'll mess my anorak."

Rosie paid and they hurried onto the pavement. The assistant's head appeared in the shop window, grotesque among loaves of bread.

"Now *she's* staring!" hissed Rosie. "How embarrassing! Fancy thinking she saw a man between us in the shop! Eat your doughnut."

So they ate, wandering, Rosie with a carrier of shopping swinging from her elbow, all her little fingers turning the doughnut as she nibbled; Andrew watching her, again seeing her as other boys might see her, with sugar on her red lips, and buttercup curls beside her eyes.

A boy blocked their way. What Father would call a youth, thought Andrew. About James's age. Stuffing the last of a sausage roll into his mouth. His nose twisted horribly as he chewed.

"Do you mind!" groaned Rosie. She stepped sideways.

The youth leaned in front of her, sneering. "Nobody to look after you now!" The sneer vanished as he choked, and Rosie danced aside as wet sausage roll hit the pavement.

Rosie held her doughnut in one hand, strode forward and slapped him on the back. He staggered. "Better?" she enquired. "Come on, Andrew."

Andrew smiled.

The boy gasped, "No time for the likes of me!"

"I should think not!" laughed Rosie.

Andrew said, "What do you mean?"

"You know! You know! Followed you, didn't I! To that war thing in the square! Nobody to look after you now!"

"So it was *you* following us," said Andrew. "And the war thing is a memorial."

The boy mimicked, "*A memorial.* Wot a posh little voice! I know it's a memorial. Where's your minder now! No time for the likes of me! I been to the baker's before you! Now I reckon you owes me a sausage roll!"

"Come on, Andrew!" sighed Rosie. "You're right," she told the boy. "We don't have time for the likes of you, and we're certainly not buying you a sausage roll—"

The boy snatched at Rosie's wrist. Her doughnut fell. Andrew gathered his fingers into a fist and strode close, but before he could strike, the boy gaped, staring behind Rosie.

Colour slipped from his cheeks leaving them white. He released her, and stepped back.

Then he turned, and fled into the crowd.

They looked at each other, Andrew and Rosie.

"Well!" gasped Rosie. "What's got into him? He's at the Bishop's Gate already!"

Andrew watched the boy dodging cars. The Bishop's Gate had two arches. One wide enough for cars, one narrow enough for pedestrians.

"Do you want a bite of my doughnut?" asked Andrew.

"No. Thanks. Oh, there's jam on my coat. Oh, well. It'll wash off in the next shower. Do you think it was really him following us? Surely he wasn't in our garden!" Rosie giggled. "Lying in wait for *me!*"

"How do you know there was someone in our garden?" Andrew frowned at Rosie. "You didn't say anything."

"You turned round. Just as you turned round to look at the church. Just as you're doing now."

"It wasn't him. At least, I don't think so. And I don't think he followed us in Broad Street. Do you?"

Rosie shrugged.

"Why did he run away?" asked Andrew.

"I don't know." Rosie rubbed sugar from her fingers, licked her lips and touched her curls. "He *might* have been in the garden."

"You don't fancy him!"

"Of course not!" She eased the carrier from her elbow and let it swing elegantly from her hand. "Come on," she said. "Since I lost my doughnut, perhaps we'll have coffee in Fountaine's."

Andrew liked Fountaine's.

He felt grown-up sitting with the white tablecloth hanging stiffly over his knees, and a waitress taking his order.

He sipped Coke while Rosie drank coffee and ate a new doughnut.

Andrew gazed down into the street. Cars growled through the Bishop's Gate. Andrew looked the other way and saw a hand removing a loaf from the baker's window.

A lot of strange things had happened.

He turned to Rosie.

"What?" she said.

"Do you always know when I'm going to speak?"

"'Speak, speak, and say thy heart's desire,'" quoted Rosie. "'Let darkness not confound thy mind—'"

"Rosie," groaned Andrew.

"What? Are you sure you don't want another doughnut? We can afford it."

"I don't want one. Did you really only push me once? Last night, in the graveyard?"

"I think so."

Andrew sighed to let Rosie know he had something to say, but he couldn't find the words.

"Out with it." Rosie stared at him over her cup.

"It was like…"

"What was like?"

"The pushing. The prodding. It was like... Oh, the way James used to push. On the stairs, suddenly, so I had to grab the bannister. Or if I was sitting, making me get up."

He watched Rosie replace her cup in its saucer. She turned her doughnut on its plate, then dabbed jam from its oozing centre and tasted it.

"He didn't mean to be cruel," she murmured. "It was fun."

Andrew tightened his mouth.

"It was!" said Rosie. "He was older than us. He didn't know that it hurt. When boys get to that age, they forget what it's like to be small. He did care about you."

Andrew said nothing. Rain swept the tearoom window.

"He always bought you a good present on your birthday," Rosie reminded him. "And at Christmas. Remember that last Christmas? A present for everybody from James! And so beautifully wrapped! That counted."

"He got me a penknife."

"I saw how much that penknife cost. Before he took the label off. He did care. Oh, I remember! I remember. You never knew this, Andrew. That boy at school. The one who bullied you?"

"When?"

"Ages ago. Norman somebody. Then he stopped bullying you. James sorted him out. He told me, but he never told anyone else. He said the only person who could push you around was him."

Andrew blew bubbles through his Coke. All he could remember of James was his prodding fingers and his voice, mocking, and bony movements urgent with strength.

"What did he say? To the boy."

"I don't know *that!*" laughed Rosie. "It was years ago. You were only seven."

"I don't remember being bullied." Except, thought Andrew, by James. "Rosie?"

"What?"

"Do you think it was James in the graveyard?"

Rosie smiled. "Prodding your shoulder? Branches, Andrew, swaying in the breeze. And the breeze blowing the newspaper."

Sometimes Rosie sounded like Mother should sound.

"It *must* have been the breeze!" she said. "Branches don't move by themselves. Newspapers don't blow about by themselves!"

She bit her doughnut.

"The branches didn't dig into *your* shoulder," said Andrew.

"Oh, don't go on about it!"

"We have to think it through!"

"You think it through!" hissed Rosie, glancing at other customers. "You're good at thinking! Just sit quietly! You're such a child!"

Andrew gaped.

Rosie glanced at him primly; bit the doughnut, lips tight as a bud. She grinned suddenly.

Andrew smiled.

"All right!" whispered Rosie as Andrew opened his mouth. "So there wasn't much of a breeze! But there's no other explanation! Oh, Gordon Niven!" she swore.

Andrew followed Rosie's gaze across the tearoom. The youth who had challenged them in the street stood in the doorway, swaggering with embarrassment.

"He's seen us!" gasped Rosie, and her cheeks reddened. She turned to the window as if the rain were interesting.

"He must have followed us again!" said Andrew.

The boy stepped awkwardly among the tables, nodding like a horse towards every corner of the room.

"*What's he doing?*" whispered Rosie to the window.

"He's coming."

The boy stopped at their table.

His hands fumbled onto the back of a chair. His fingernails had been nibbled to the living flesh.

Andrew said, "What do you want? Are you following my sister? We'll tell the police." Rosie's head moved.

The boy jerked the chair out from the table and sat down. His lower lip rolled and unrolled as if it had a life of its own. Rainwater moved in his hair.

"I'm not following *her*," he muttered.

Rosie faced him. "Then go away!"

"It's not you! Not you! Think yourself lucky! Fine chance!"

"Oh, shut up!" said Andrew. "What do you want?"

"I've seen you two around the town."

"Get lost!" sighed Rosie.

"You're James's brother and sister."

Rosie sat still.

The boy's bitten fingers pushed at a table knife. He jumped as a waitress appeared. He shook his head, and she left. He stared around, shifting in his seat to see behind him. His knee bobbed, making the stiff tablecloth rustle, and around his lips, his face was white.

"Are you ill?" asked Andrew.

"No—"

"How did you know James?" demanded Rosie. She mocked him: "He wouldn't have time for the likes of you!"

"Shut up, Rosie. He doesn't look well—"

"At school," said the boy. "He was older than me. I saw him!"

Something sank in Andrew's stomach.

The boy searched again, around the tearoom. He said, "How did you do it? Come on. He's dead, isn't he? You got another brother? His twin? Why isn't he here? Where'd he go? Sticks to you like glue, doesn't he? I saw him! I saw 'im in the street! Hands on your shoulders! Taking care of you! I saw 'im! Sometimes y'can't see him! *Grinning like a lunatic!*"

3

Saturday lunch-time.
Rosie finds something to scream about,
and the butcher talks of a ghost.

Andrew knew what the boy had said.

At least, he knew what the words meant; that James had been with him and Rosie in the street; and difficult to see. No wonder that woman had stared, then the mother and her little girl.

But Andrew couldn't understand what it meant. Was it James who had followed them from the vicarage? And stood with them in the baker's?

Andrew looked at Rosie to see if she was awake to what was happening.

Rosie's mouth opened, but silence lingered between her and the youth.

Chatter from other tables rang in Andrew's ears. He heard the till bleep at the tearoom door.

"Oh, no!" Tears swarmed down Rosie's cheeks. Her hands shook as she half raised them to her face. "Why," she moaned at the boy. "Why are you saying these terrible things?"

"Wot— ?"

"You *horrible— !*"

"Rosie!" whispered Andrew. "Rosie, don't!"

She grabbed her cup as she would grab a stone, and raised it threateningly. Andrew lunged, his hand fumbling over hers.

Coffee flooded his fingers, staining the tablecloth. Rosie struggled. Sobs burst from her pulled-down mouth. The table tilted. "Rosie!"

The boy got up. "You leave me be!"

Rosie tore her hand free and raised the cup again.

The waitress hurried near. "Rosie!" pleaded Andrew.

"Get out!" said the waitress. "Go on! Pay at the desk! Then get out!" The boy left. "You as well. You ought to know better! I know who you are all right! Your father will hear about this! Get going! Take your carrier!"

"We're going!" said Andrew. "Rosie, you have the money. Don't cry! Give me the shopping. Oh, Rosie. And we've still to go to the butcher's!"

They stood in the street doorway of Fountaine's, Rosalind with her face to the door-post, weeping, Andrew holding her coat sleeve to comfort her, trying to pretend to passers-by that nothing was wrong.

He watched the boy on the other side of Main Street looking back. The boy gestured foully then went striding, until Andrew lost sight of him.

Andrew sighed. Why don't people *think*, he wondered. What good does lifting his fingers do? What good does Rosie do attacking him? People should *talk*.

James had talked to Norman; stopped his

bullying; though Andrew couldn't remember Norman.

But people were afraid. The boy was afraid; confronting them in the street when he thought they were unprotected. Rosie's yellow curls would have attracted him. But even *he* tried to talk. That's why he had come into the tearoom.

Andrew wasn't afraid. Maybe, he thought, that's why I talk. Surely talking is better than hurting people?

"I'm ready," whispered Rosie. "What a *pig!*"

"Stop it, Rosie. Please. Are we going to the butcher's?"

"To the butcher's," she agreed.

"Through the arch then."

"I know where it is!" Rosie drew in a long shuddering breath. "Has he gone?"

"Yes."

"This way!"

"I know where it is," said Andrew.

They walked under the arch of the Bishop's Gate into the new town. *The Weaver's Cottage* – with a National Trust plaque screwed into its stonework – leaned against the outside of the town wall; the last remaining cottage of an ancient row. The shadow of a tree darkened the corner where the cottage and the town wall joined.

Andrew and Rosie crossed at traffic lights and entered the shopping arcade.

They hurried to the butcher's and stood in the queue.

Andrew looked around.

Too many real people, he decided, to allow space for James's ghost; if it *was* James's ghost prodding his shoulder in the graveyard, then – this morning – following them through the town. Andrew fluffed out a little laugh. What nonsense.

And yet...

Strip lights exposed every corner of the arcade. It really was bright after the pale daylight outside. Andrew wondered how much electricity this huge place used.

A strip light flickered and died.

Nearby, the shoe shop window vanished into gloom as its lights popped, spraying glass over the shoes. A woman in the shop ran out, stuck her hands angrily to her waist, then strode inside.

Another strip light pulsed.

The glitter of an artificial waterfall diminished, as lights behind the water faded one by one.

Then a spotlight high on the arcade wall exploded, showering glass. A young man yelped and bent forward, broken glass on his back. Women picked at his hair, laughing and the young man allowed himself to be cleaned.

"Like monkeys," said Andrew.

Rosie grinned.

"Always something," moaned the butcher. "What can I get you?"

"A large steak pie, please."

Andrew's eyes wandered to the darkened shoe shop window.

In the window, among the shoes, was the old man who had sat under the war memorial.

"But he can't—" said Andrew.

"And four pork chops. Who can't?" asked Rosie.

Andrew glanced at his sister, then pointed at the shop window.

"What?" said Rosie.

But the window was full of shoes.

"Huh! I'm seeing things. I thought the old man was in the shop window."

"What old man? Oh, I see him," said Rosie.

"Where?"

"Behind the waterfall. And a pound of sausages, please."

"How did he get there?" Andrew frowned, "I must have seen his reflection. I suppose it is him? I couldn't see him properly at the memorial. There goes another spotlight! What's happening!"

People squealed and ran from the exploding fragments.

A triangle of glass dropped at Andrew's feet.

"Here!" said the butcher. "That was close. Can't risk contaminating my meat with light bulbs!"

"It's the only bit that came this far." Andrew picked up the glass.

"Let me see," said the butcher. "That's funny."

"What is?" asked Andrew.

Rosie was reading her shopping list.

"This ain't part of a light bulb. It's flat. It must be the casing. The glass over the front of the bulb. Keeps it clean. Fancy that breaking. Wot a blooming mess. I told them they shouldn't put that waterfall there. It's a mockery, that's wot it is."

"What do you mean?" asked Rosie. "Could I have half a pound of turkey-on-the-bone? Have other things happened?"

"I'll pop this glass in the bin. Half-pound-turkey-on-the-bone coming up. I'll tell you wot I mean, young lady. This arcade was build over the Bishop's Well. And there are some pretty stories, I can tell you, about that well."

The butcher frowned as he sliced turkey. He dropped the slices on the scale.

Andrew waited for the butcher to speak again, but he wrapped the turkey and handed it to Rosie.

"What did you mean," asked Rosie, "about the waterfall being a mockery?"

"Another time, miss. Here's your change. Yes, madam?"

Rosie wandered, putting money in her purse, struggling with her carrier of meat. "Hold this a minute." Andrew took the carrier. "What's the time?" asked Rosie.

Andrew found the arcade clock. "Nearly twelve."

"We need veg."

She frowned. "You sit over there at the café. Get another Coke."

"I'm hungry."

"Get a scone."

"Where are you going?"

"For the veg. I want you to sit where you can watch for the butcher. It must be nearly his lunch-time."

"Watch for the butcher?"

"Andrew, I want to know about the Bishop's Well. OK?"

"Why— ?"

"I'll help you with the carriers. Come on." They crossed to tables in front of the café. "Sit here.

Aren't these plants nice? If the butcher appears, talk to him. Or are you too shy?"

"Of course not. But— "

"D'you want a Coke?"

"And a meringue."

Rosie went to the café counter. She returned with a Coke and a scone and butter.

"Better for you."

"Oh, Rosie."

"I'll be back soon."

Andrew sipped the Coke. A woman pushed a floor brush through the crowd, sweeping up glass. No more lights had burst.

The butcher listened to a customer.

Andrew looked at the tropical plants, like giant green feather dusters, growing in the artificial garden beside him. He wondered why Rosie wanted to know about the Bishop's Well.

He decided he *would* speak to the butcher; if he left the shop. Rosie was usually right.

The butcher thudded at meat, half-hidden behind the counter. It was after twelve. Perhaps his lunch-time was half past.

Andrew ate his scone. Two men manoeuvred stepladders among the shoppers. They stood the ladders up under the dead strip lights.

Andrew watched the men replacing the lights; shrugging over the spotlights. When the spotlights came on, a shadow filled the artificial garden. Andrew moved his chair away from it. The men entered the shoe shop.

Andrew thought perhaps he should move his

chair further from the plants. Or rather, from the gloom that stood among them. Not that it was real gloom. He could see perfectly well, the stems of the plants and the texture of the earth around them. It didn't look like real earth; not like the earth in the garden at home. Or in the graveyard.

The gloom seemed to have spread across his table. He tried to think about what that boy had said, but his brain sat slow in his head. Rosie would say that all the excitement was tiring him. He *was* tired, suddenly.

He could really, really sleep. Right here.

The arcade was warm.

Was somebody screaming?

Far away a girl's voice rang with terror. It trilled under the arcade's roof; but Andrew was too sleepy to look up. A murmur of questions billowed around him, like people asking What is it? What's wrong? And, Let her past.

The scream changed, its wordless howl turning into his name.

Andrew.

Rosie?

Rosie is screaming my name.

Andrew forced his eyes up. The gloom from the plants darkened his vision. He saw people looking at him, moving back, making way, and something, oh, still at the waterfall, rushing towards him, but slowly. Was it slowly? Flapping. But flapping darkly, not white like the thing in the graveyard. That stupid newspaper. This was a giant Rosie-bat, her coat flying, a carrier bag dropping from her hand, spewing vegetables across the floor, potatoes bouncing on the tiles. A jar of pickle hit the tiles and stuck.

Rosie flew nearer, growing darker and larger.

She came, large as night, and fear touched Andrew; and suddenly her scream was real, exploding in his ears, and her coat engulfed him, and astonishment swept the fear aside as Rosie's warm body crashed against his, knocking him backwards out of his chair, smashing him to the floor, Rosie thudding on top of him, her shrieks hot on his face. Then she was off him and her fists gathered the front of his anorak as she crawled, pulling him across the tiles, pushing him out of the gloom; screaming and swearing.

People closed around them.

Rosie knelt.

"*You silly little fool! Why didn't you run? He was reaching for you!*"

Are you hurt, dear?

"Reaching...?"

Andrew found Rosie's face blazing close to his, her mouth hauled out of shape.

Here's the girl's shopping. You've lost some potatoes, young lady, and your pickle's all over the floor.

Andrew smelled fresh meat, and a large soft hand gripped his arm, lifting him. A red and white striped apron bulged into his gaze. "I served these kids a little while ago," said the butcher. "Bring them into my back shop. Take it easy, you two. She's crying her heart out. Did anybody see anything?"

She was running.

"Come into the back shop. We don't need anybody else, thanks. My wife'll look after 'em. Here we are. Sit in this chair, young lady. Oo's this? Ah. Thank you. Somebody brought your other carrier bags. That was kind. I think a spot of tea's called for. Harry, you get back to the counter and serve my customers. Doris – that's my Doris, for you. Soon as there's an upset, she's got the kettle on. Drink this. No need to talk. You can wash your faces at the sink. There's paper towels. That lass is crying fit to bust. And the little chap's got a face on 'im like a pound of suet."

Tea plunged heat down inside Andrew.

"Doris is asking if we can phone home for you."

"I'm all right," said Andrew.

Rosie shook her head. Andrew knew she was thinking of Mother, who would panic if a stranger phoned, and Father, who would explain everything.

What did Rosie mean about someone reaching for him? He had been dozing, almost. Had he finished his Coke? He remembered shifting his chair out of the gloom that hovered among the plants, then the gloom seemed to creep over the table. He imagined long dark arms embracing him, hauling him into a sleep from which he would never wake.

"Rosie!"

"I'm here. The butcher's gone into the front shop. You should have run." Rosie gulped at her tea.

"I didn't see anything."

"It was the old man!" hissed Rosie. "Like a shadow! Reaching— !"

"Here we are then!" The butcher bustled in. He

gave them a plate with sandwiches overflowing with cold ham.

"Oh, thank you!" gasped Andrew. He didn't understand about the old man. Then the sandwich made him realize how hungry he was, despite the doughnut and the scone.

The butcher sat. He said to Rosie, "Want to tell me about it?"

Rosie's head trembled.

"Don't blame you. Eat your sandwich. I've seen things," sighed the butcher. "You up to hearing this? I won't tell you if you ain't. Sure? All right.

"Now then. You ought to be here first thing of a winter's morning, when there's no daylight, just them strip lights. 'Tain't natural with just strip lights. And nobody in this whole huge empty place.

"It don't sound much when you say it, but I've seen things. Wot things? I don't know. Shadows that don't stand still like shadows should. And glowing things; not *things* as such; more just like dots glowing, like cats' eyes. But when you look straight at 'em, why, they're gone.

"The worst place is behind the waterfall. What a sight it is! Ugliest object I ever seen, and it supposed to be for looking at. Water's pumped up at the back, and cascades down the front, and silly fools chuck good money in and make wishes. Well, round the back – where the water pumps up – that's the darkest place. Oh, it's lit bright enough! But them strip lights – take my word for it – don't do what daylight does. Shows up things we ain't supposed to see and lets in shadows that ought not to be let in. I hope I'm not scaring you?"

Andrew stared.

Rosalind stuffed the end of her sandwich into her mouth.

"Well." The butcher reached for the teapot and filled himself a mug. "'Tain't quite hot, but it's wet. And let me tell you something else. I think I mentioned it when I served you.

"Before this arcade was built, I warned 'em. I warned the surveyors who came to measure the site. I warned the town council who gave planning permission. I warned the builders when they started digging the foundations. The Bishop's Well, I told 'em, is right there and no good will come of you interfering with it.

"They laughed. Or paid no attention. The Bishop's Well supplies water for that bl— sorry, that ugly-looking fountain."

"But why did you warn them?" asked Andrew. "How did you know anything would happen? Are you sure— ?"

"Sure? Sure? You sit there and ask me if I'm sure? Ask your sister! She didn't come running all across the arcade screaming fit to bring the roof down because she wasn't sure! Have some tea. Oh, I'm sure. And the reason I knew before was that I'd seen things before. Why d'you think I've got a shop here? Because I wasn't given no choice!

"I had my father's shop fifteen years back. All Victorian tiles inside and timber black as treacle. But the buildings were a bit run-down and town planners was treated like princes! So the old buildings came down and this place put up, and either I came here or went out of business."

"But—"

"But the Bishop's Well was in a lane in those days. With a little brass sink and a brass cup the shape of a flower chained to the wall. Anybody could drink there. But I don't know any who ever did. Nobody'll come creeping down a back lane looking for water, will they? And if they found the well by chance, my goodness! would you drink in the darkest corner, with stones dripping with moss, and the water whispering out o' solid rock?"

"You said you saw things," said Andrew.

"Once. I'll be honest. Some folk stretch the truth. Once was enough. It's hard for you to picture now, but the well was where the fountain is, and the lane went through the shoe shop. The end of the lane wouldn't be far off where you was sitting, young man, having your sleep. And my shop was a few yards round the corner. About where Woollies is now.

"Long time ago, this was. Me and Doris was courting. I'd been cutting up carcasses all day and I was fair exhausted. I was last out of the shop, and by that time the sun was well down. Doris, she came to meet me. I remember clear as if it was yesterday. She said, 'Ben, you're done in. Give me them keys, then you're coming home with me for a cup of tea and a right old feed.'

"She took the keys and started locking the shop door. I didn't argue. Real good idea it sounded. I wandered along the pavement. Doris was having some difficulty with the top lock. I got to the corner where the lane led to the Bishop's Well. There was just one lamp post in the lane and it so stuck with grime it only made the darkness darker.

"Now." The butcher leaned forward. "I haven't told many people this. They'd say I'd been drinking. But I'm telling you cos of what happened today. And I'd be obliged if you didn't spread this story around."

"We won't," breathed Andrew.

"Where I was standing," said the butcher, "was well-enough lit for them days, but – as I said – the lane was pretty much in darkness. The first thing I knew was a chill all over my skin as if an icy wind had whipped up round the corner. I wasn't thinking about anything in particular – probably about the feed my Doris was going give me; so what I saw didn't pop out of my imagination, you understand, and into the street. I was waiting at the corner, facing down the lane.

"By the light of the lamp post I could see the cobbles and the dark nook with the well water rustling. Someone walked past me.

"Seemed to come from behind me, then he was walking down the lane. Well, I was shivering with the chills, and when this figure swept by without so much as a 'Good night' or 'Howdydo', I fair jumped. Then I took a hard look and I remember thinking how long his coat was; anyways, something dark was hanging around him. Then it dawned on me, 'e was a priest, in one o' them black gown things. Though I wouldn't swear to it.

"I said, 'Good night, Father.' Not that I'm of the faith, mind you, but I was that startled. I felt I had to say something.

"He didn't turn. He didn't answer. Just walked on.

"By the time I spoke again he was under the lamp post. The light shone on his head. He had white hair. I can see it yet. And when I said 'Good night, Father,' again, he paused under the light.

"I knew he was going to turn. I knew, too, that if I saw his face..."

The butcher placed his mug on the floor.

"He began to turn. The light caught the top of his ear. Then his cheek. I tell you, the chills were rushing about my skin like nobody's business, but I couldn't look away. His shoulders started to turn, as if to finish it, you know! face me and devil take the consequences! Then *thump!* A hand lands on my back, and I tell you I near collapsed onto the pavement. But it was only my Doris. She said, 'Ben, I was talking to you. You must be asleep on your feet, poor lamb.' And she led me away.

"The priest was gone. I suppose he could've moved out of sight while I was half-fainting, but I don't believe it. And what sort of face I'd have seen, I can't imagine. But I think it would've done for me. I think –" he leaned his forearm on his knee and stared at Rosie and Andrew "– I think I would have dropped down dead."

The sky lay thick over the town.

A wind stirred the grass among the standing stones. It pushed through the new town, carrying more rain, turning up coat collars, bending umbrellas. It leaned on shop windows all down Main Street; it stuck a paper bag to the war memorial.

It swept along Broad Street, and prowled around

the church; and the wind's hollow voice called into the chimneys of the vicarage.

In the vicarage sitting-room, the Reverend Ainsley glanced at flames wriggling in the fireplace.

Then he sat still.

He sat so long that Andrew fidgeted, making Rosie glare at him to be patient.

"Well," said Father at last, "I've heard some excuses for being late for lunch, but this takes the biscuit."

A joke.

Andrew tightened his lips.

"It's too much," said Father to himself.

"What is?" asked Rosie.

Father's eyebrows raised themselves out of a frown. "Everything you've told me, Rosie, is too much. I could explain the flapping thing in the graveyard as a newspaper." His hand moved towards the kitchen where the pedal bin had swallowed the paper last night. "Even if it *was* unlikely to blow in the breeze. I could explain somebody following you from the house here, to the shops – maybe someone *did* follow you – for whatever reason. And the old man appearing so suddenly at the war memorial... Perhaps he could move quicker than you anticipated.

"And the boy – the youth – could have been trying to annoy you with his story about James. Then what you saw in the arcade, Rosie, must have been an illusion – the old man in the shadow among the plants, reaching out – what? *monstrously?* for Andrew. That can't be real – even though it sent you screaming." Father frowned again.

"And the butcher's tale… Well, it was just a tale. To make you feel better, perhaps. You know. Sharing an experience. But the problem," his voice reached the back of the room as Rosie's mouth opened, "is that *too many* things are happening. Explaining them one by one is all very well, but they didn't happen one by one. They arrived in a bunch – since yesterday evening. And that worries me."

Father stared at nothing.

Andrew looked at Rosie. She ignored him.

Flames stretched up the chimney.

Rain rattled on the windows.

Rosie said, "Is this about James?" and Father's stare focused on her.

"Yes," said Father. Then he bowed his head and his breath came swiftly. Rosie knelt at his knee and put her arm around him.

"I'm all right, Rosie. Thank you. Sit in your chair. You're good children. And so was James. Oh, he was." Father nodded at Andrew. "I'm not just saying that. He had a remarkable mind. He could talk to the doctor for hours – Doctor John, I mean – and leave him bewildered. Not with youthful nonsense. He would dip into books and remember facts … oh, about anything, from any place, from any time, and bring them together in unexpected ways. Do you know the greatest love," Father's voice rang trembling around the furniture, and flames in the fireplace shook their fists, "is to give your life, willingly, for someone else?"

Mother's step sounded in the hall, and Father stopped talking.

The door opened. "Lunch," said Mother, "though I'm not sure if tinned soup is proper food for you two. Your cheeks were so pale when that woman brought you home. You're very quiet?"

"Coming," said Father beaming, gathering Andrew and Rosie, guiding them into the kitchen.

Andrew looked up, and Father gulped beneath his smile. Andrew wished they could discuss James in front of Mother.

"It was kind of her," said Mother.

"Doris," said Rosie, eating tomato soup. "The butcher's wife. I couldn't have walked home carrying the shopping. Not after..."

"I don't suppose it was anything," said Mother cheerfully, "though I wish you'd been here to make the lunch, Rosalind. My head was no better. The soup's not burnt?"

"No," said Rosie.

Andrew kept in a sigh; the soup wasn't even hot.

"You should taste some," Father told Mother, and his eye found Andrew and bunched into the tiniest wink. Andrew smiled. Father approved of nobody-complaining about the soup.

Andrew said to Mother, "Couldn't you bake a chocolate sponge?"

"Oh, my goodness, that was a long time ago." Mother escaped across the kitchen. "Pizzas. I sometimes think we should get a microwave. But the Rayburn's wonderful. You like cooking on the Rayburn, don't you, Rosie? Rosalind, you like cooking on the Rayburn –"

Rosie sobbed, her head down over her soup plate.

Andrew watched as Mother hurried to embrace Rosie. Father rested his spoon, his face softening.

"Rosie, Rosie," squeaked Mother. Her too-young hair hid one eye as she looked at Father. Her mouth opened, but she didn't speak; she didn't know what to say to comfort Rosie.

Father reached, and pushed Mother's hair aside. He said, "You always do the right thing, Mary." Then he went to the Rayburn, and served the pizzas.

Andrew left the kitchen.

He felt his slippers tug into each carpeted step on the stairs. He heard Father's voice bright above the clatter of dishes. On the eighth step he straightened James's watercolour of the standing stones. He had straightened it already today; when he and Rosie had rushed to go shopping. He looked down into the hall.

The carpet was threadbare where he and Rosie (and James!) always jumped the last few steps. He went down to the fourth step and jumped. He went up to the fifth step. Rosie jumped from the fifth step. There was no reason why Andrew couldn't. He gripped the bannister and leapt.

He clung to the bannister as he flew down. He let go too late, twisted in the air, and landed on one foot. He sprawled, thudding his shoulder onto the carpet.

"Oh!"

Father laughed in the kitchen.

Andrew sat up. He went to the fifth step and jumped without holding the bannister. He landed, crouching.

He jumped once more, confidently. Then he ran up the stairs, pausing at James's painting. He pushed it straight again. His jumping must have moved it. Andrew still didn't like the grass blowing so wildly around the standing stones.

Outside, the wind sighed against the front door.

Andrew wished – for a moment – that he was more sensitive, like Rosie. She had wanted to ask the butcher about the bishop – as if she knew it was important. But the butcher had told them a ghost story. About a priest?

Would the butcher know the difference between a bishop and a priest?

"Huh!" said Andrew.

And he stood on the stairs, not thinking exactly, but wondering.

Then he went to James's room.

4

Saturday afternoon.
Andrew is afraid of a piece of paper;
and Mother bakes a chocolate sponge.

Doctor John's book lay on James's table, the map showing the ley line, shut fast inside.

Andrew glanced around at James's book shelves. He really wanted to know about the bishop. Doris had hurried Rosie and Andrew into her car before they had asked the butcher.

Andrew couldn't see a volume on local history.

He opened Doctor John's book, and found a photograph of a woman holding a forked stick before her, and walking across a field. He remembered that dowsing was using a forked stick to find water under the ground.

He read about Doctor John discovering his dowsing ability. A child had left a chestnut on a string in the surgery, and while idly twirling the chestnut near a torch (which the doctor had just used to look down the child's throat), he discovered that the string swung vigorously despite his efforts to hold it steady, responding – presumably – to the electricity in the torch. Experimenting more seriously, the doctor found that the string reacted to subtle energies in the earth by spinning either gently or not so gently according to the amount of energy.

Andrew turned some pages.

"Hauntings on the Ley Line" said a chapter heading. Andrew sat at the table.

Many hauntings have been reported over the centuries, within the area of the ley line. The people who saw ghosts, black dogs, mysterious lights, and other phenomena, were not aware, of course, that the ley line existed, because the ley theory was only postulated in the 1920s by Alfred Watkins.

However, my most exciting find was a manuscript bound in an old volume in the basement of the local library which suggests that the energy of the ley line was not only known about – but was being deliberately used. The manuscript was dictated by a groom in the service of Bishop Redman in the eighteenth century, to a notary. It was duly signed by the groom, witnessed, and dated 3rd November 1794.

Most interestingly, the groom insisted that the manuscript should not be made public until after his death, and also after the death of the bishop, in case of reprisals.

I give the groom's story in full, in my own words, but retaining, I hope, some of the flavour of the time. The groom tells of an uncertain atmosphere in and around the bishop's palace, shortly after the bishop's arrival to take over the duties of the prebend.

The bishop was a smiling man, elderly, with a strong figure. He showed small kindnesses to his staff, but despite this, no one fully trusted him. The only solid reason given was that animals were nervous of him, though later, he was disposed to rages, laying about him with a riding crop.

Several rooms in the palace were set aside by the bishop, as a laboratory. He let it be known that he was researching the healing qualities of physics and potions, and indeed he spent many hours during spring and summer gathering herbs with his own hand, both in the herb garden and in the countryside, and the palace was filled with the perfume thereof.

But still no one trusted him. The groom's first fright was in the winter of 1793 in the second year of the bishop's occupancy.

The night was freezing, and the moon three-quarters full. The groom was doing his rounds of the stables when a woman's screams "rose to the stars". One Peggy Keller, a scullion, ran from the direction of the herb garden, her skirts held clear of her feet the better she could run, and without hesitation clung to the groom so that he almost dropped his lantern. And she cried most piteously, pleading that he should save her, for she had stood face to face with Satan himself.

The groom was afraid, because the girl was known to be intelligent, though, of course, uneducated and full of superstition. He questioned her, at the same time holding his lantern high on a pole to cast more light, but she repeated that she had seen Satan, and kept pointing in the direction of the herb garden.

The groom – as much to prove his bravery to himself as to the wench – insisted that they return to the garden, but before he could persuade the girl to go with him, other servants appeared, fearful, demanding to know who was screaming.

Peggy Keller had gone outside (from the kitchen where she slept) to obey a call of nature. Then being fully awake, had walked a little way in the moonlight, venturing into the herb garden. She had heard a rustling, and thinking of seeing perhaps a badger, she stood still.

She heard the rustling again, but realized it came not from the ground but high up, as if on the wall that enclosed the orchard. So she looked.

The moonlight shone bright on the wall, showing every brick, and showing also a dark lump about the size of a sack of mangolds draped on the top of the wall.

She was wondering why a sack should be in such a strange place, when it seemed, in the moonlight, that a leg descended from the sack – as a resting cat might let one leg dangle. But the object was bigger than any cat.

Being not without courage, Peggy Keller stepped closer, following the path among the garden beds, glancing down to see that she did not stumble.

When she looked again, the sack had gone.

She stood motionless, her heart fluttering, looking hard along the top of the wall.

She could not see the sack. Then her eye alighted on a shadow at the foot of the wall, taller than the herbs growing there.

Then the shadow stood up, the height of a child, but of a shape most repulsive, and its eyes shone, seemingly with a light of their own.

Peggy Keller ran, her skin cold with horror, and only when she was clear of the herb garden did she find her voice, and begin screaming.

The groom and several other male servants investigated the garden, but found no sign of any animal or other visitant, though one claimed to smell brimstone – but he was known as a romancer.

The chill of James's room had crept into Andrew's flesh. Beyond the curtains, a leaf clung to the wet glass.

Andrew lifted the book and went downstairs. Across the hall from the sitting-room, in the study, Father's voice preached gently, practising tomorrow's sermon.

A teacup clinked in the kitchen. Mother would be reading a magazine.

In the sitting-room, a slope of coal glowed in the fireplace, and a red-lit mound on the rug was Rosie, her head on a cushion, Father's coat over her, for she was exhausted after her fright in the arcade. She sighed as Andrew climbed into an armchair; but she didn't wake.

"I'm finding out about the bishop," whispered Andrew, then huddled down to the story.

The groom's second fright concerned the well.

(The well was not a hole in the ground, but rather a spring arising out of rocks, and readers who are no longer teenagers may remember the Bishop's Well in Knock Lane. It is now somewhere under the arcade in the new town, feeding the plastic waterfall. The bishop's palace was approximately where Woolworth's is now, the original bishop despising the protection of the town wall when he built the palace, demonstrating his faith in God's protection, rather than the protection of mortar and stone.)

Tom Keene (the groom) was working in the stable yard. A pale sun sat on the horizon, and mist lay waist-deep on the cobbles; hoofs clattered, and the jangle of harness and the smell and puffing of the horses were a delight. The dawn chorus sang at its full-throated loudest.

In those days the well ran into a pool that drained to no-one-knew-where deep in the earth. And culverts diverted water from the pool to all parts of the garden, emptying into a stream a mile away. The well itself stood among trees.

In several places throughout the gardens, the water fell over prettily-constructed stone ledges, high enough to get a bucket under. (Though few would risk the bishop's eye on them if they dared.) However, one such place was provided close to the kitchen; but the water there, on occasion, ran muddy, and the cook would insist on water direct from the well.

Folk had always complained about fetching water from the well; they didn't mind the ten minute walk to get there, for that was ten minutes of not working, but they did mind carrying two buckets heavy with water with just a length of rope over their shoulders to take the weight; and as often as not, half the water would spill onto their feet, then they had to return for more; wet feet and all. The only person who didn't mind was Lazenby.

Lazenby was big. Five foot ten inches, with long arms, thick as branches. He was dull-witted, but of a good disposition. Lazenby would do anything if you asked him kindly.

Tom Keene had made a friend of Lazenby; not a friend you would meet when work was done and you needed to chat, but a friend to share a slice of beef and a loaf of bread in the middle of the day.

Concerning this summer's morning in 1794 (that is, the summer following the winter when Peggy saw the demon in the herb garden); Lazenby had been to the well, but he had spilled most of the water hurrying back to the kitchen, which was unlike him – for two reasons. One: he never hurried. And two: he seldom spilled more than a drop.

The cook asked, what was the matter with him? but she was too busy to listen to the poor dullard and told him to fetch more water. Imagine her astonishment when he refused. He would only go if Tom Keene went with him, for he had seen the bishop's ghost.

Some folk laughed – though not loud in case they got sent instead – and some shook their heads. And the cook shook Lazenby, saying that it was a strange ghost with the bishop not dead but working in his laboratory.

But the upshot was, Tom Keene went to the spring with Lazenby.

The groom could get little sense out of Lazenby, who glowered at Tom's questions, and rattled his buckets.

When they neared the spring, Lazenby tarried, leaving Tom to walk into the trees himself. The trees were mainly birch, and their silver bark and dainty leaves seemed friendly enough in the morning sunshine.

But the rock was black. The water from the rock tumbled into a pool where bubbles and ripples glittered on the surface. And Tom Keene hesitated. He reports that – despite the sun sliding brightly among the trees – the spring and pool lay in shadow, as if something hung above among the trees' branches; but there was nothing.

"Why, man," he said to Lazenby – who still delayed – "there is nought here to frighten a child!" The groom smiled, encouraging his friend forward; but admits that he was uneasy in himself. "The cook will have our heads if we don't fill the buckets! Pass one to me if you are afraid of a shadow!"

So Lazenby passed a bucket to Tom, and Tom held it under the spring, scooping a handful to drink: and it was sweet and cold. "And now the other!" And he swung the second bucket over the pool to fill it.

He says:

Something held my foot. I thought I'd put my toe under a root. There were plenty buried beneath last autumn's leaves. I leaned one hand on the rock, still reaching with the bucket. Then I heard Lazenby thudding away, crashing among the birches, moaning in that stupid voice of his.

I shouted, "Have your wits left you altogether?" I was about to scold him for leaving me to do his job. The bucket was near full by now.

I jerked my foot back to release it from the root, but a sudden weariness overcame me, and it seemed not to matter that my foot was grasped, for the darkness which overhung the pool filled my mind. Then the bucket became too heavy, and in my daze I let it swing against my shin.

The splash of icy water into my boots brought me to my senses.

The darkness cleared, leaving the pool sparkling

and the trees silver. And I glanced down, rubbing my shin, and amid the ripples I saw five tiny round objects close together – like the tips of fingers – descending under the water. But I knew my eyes were deceived, for they added not to the ripples on the water's surface.

On the rug, under Father's coat, Rosie moaned in her sleep.

The fire flared, throwing shadows amid the cool daylight.

Andrew switched on a table lamp.

He turned a page.

Tom Keene, throwing off the darkness from his mind, filled both buckets, having picked up the one Lazenby dropped when he fled; he attached the rope for his shoulders, then returned to the kitchen with the water, and asked Lazenby why he had run. But Lazenby refused to say that day, only muttering, "'Twas the bishop" over and over; and never did tell until the end of his life.

The final part of the groom's testament is certainly very strange.

As a researcher of ghosts and other phenomena, I have found that the witness who talks a lot is perhaps less than reliable, the "evidence" growing with each telling of his (or her) story.

But Tom Keene's statement has a restraint which I, personally, find convincing. And if the next part of the groom's tale is true, who knows what is lurking, even today, in the ley line that cuts our town in half?

The Groom's Story. (The night of the following events was about four weeks after the incident at the well.)

I saw Sir Martin Bentlock close to, twice, while he was alive.

I heard the crashing of carriage wheels on the drive at the front of the palace. "Someone has died!" I said, for why else would anyone drive their team so hard?

I ran to tend the horses.

The poor beasts had been driven to a standstill, their limbs a-tremble, steam rising from their bodies, their breath frothing around the bits. I talked quietly to calm them, patting their necks, asking the driver what disaster has overtaken us? but he glared, his look silencing me; and a footman unfolded the carriage steps and Sir Martin Bentlock descended to the drive.

I have seen the gargoyles on the great minster in York, and thought that the stone masons who fashioned those hideous heads possessed an imagination deserving respect.

But perhaps they had met Sir Martin Bentlock.

Never have I seen human flesh sculptured into such wickedness; and not merely the wickedness of selfishness (which we all share to some extent); but I perceived a wickedness that delights in hurting God's creatures.

You can be sure that I gave those horses the finest care; and I would have sought out the driver and beaten him as he had beaten them, for blood oozed with the sweat on the poor beasts' hides; but Master Lamb, the head groom, bade me attend my duties.

And perhaps, after all, it was not the driver's fault, but the fault of Sir Martin; for there was not – as I had first thought – a disaster; Sir Martin Bentlock, I learned, drove his horses at full gallop wherever he went; and if the horses died, why, he would buy more.

Gossip provided me with further details of Sir Martin's cruelty. These details are not part of this testimony, because I know not of them with my own eyes, though I believe them to be true, for Sir Martin had the eccentricity of talking aloud to himself without thought to who was in his presence. But one thing I knew as fact: the bishop and Sir Martin were busy in the laboratory.

During all the years of the bishop's residency his good works were known from York to Bristol, but we who lived close to him were unable to rid ourselves of a natural fear of him; and the fear was enhanced by the smells and sounds in the laboratory – smells other than those of herbal remedies.

"Things what's good for a body," Peggy said to me on many an evening, "should smell sweet, not stink like the fires of Hell. Stands to reason, Tom Keene. And why would my lord bishop rage behind locked doors fit to send the maids running and weeping with their aprons over their heads? He knows too much. Mark my words –" and she would turn her sweet face up to mine, serious and fearful "– he knows too much."

And I would tease her, for I knew the tittle-tattle, saying, "Yes, my love, he wants what ain't right for mortal man. He wants to live for ever!"

But I could not turn her from such nonsense. And the gossip persisted, though quietly enough, for no harm came to anyone, and we were all well fed.

Sir Martin Bentlock's visit had extended into

several weeks. The summer burnt bright, and evenings lingered into night. Master Lamb (I say no wrong of him, for his love of the horses makes him attend soberly to his duties) but Master Lamb is happy in his wine, and on occasion I have found him asleep in the courtyard, or even laid out on the road from the inn, like a felled log, in danger of being run over by a carriage leaving the town. So I keep a weather eye on him.

One night, he was late returning, so I strolled out. And the stars danced, and the moon laid silver on the fields. The town wall bulged black and the road was striped with trees' shadows, but I walked, enjoying the night-time scents, and smiling at the *who–oo* of an owl.

I reached the gateway in the town wall, and looked about me.

I saw the lights of the inn, far along Broad Street. And candles burned in some windows of the nearer Main Street. Distantly I heard the voice of the watchman calling that all was well. Then I looked behind me, and spied a hand on the road, and the sleeve disappearing into a shadow at the roots of a tree. I recognized the hand as that of Master Lamb and regretted having passed him in the dark. I approached, saying, "Master Lamb? Is that you? 'Tis I, Tom Keene."

Then I saw that the hand was palm-down on the road, and the fingers bent as if digging into the earth, and this struck me as queer, for a drunk man lies limp. So I hastened to lean over him, and was astonished to find his eyes on me, staring; then he clung to me, shivering, sober as when he'd set out, saying he'd been overcome by a darkness thicker than the night, and moaning that he'd seen the bishop, he'd seen the bishop.

And I said, "Master Lamb, whoever you saw, it wasn't the bishop, for he is in his laboratory. The lights are still burning."

But he clung to me, did Master Lamb – and him so strict during the day – and insisted he had seen the bishop, and he kept glancing up into the trees as if the bishop might be clambering about there, like a squirrel. And I asked why he was so afraid, for the bishop had never been known to harm any man.

But he spoke no more of it and thanked me for coming to meet him, and we walked home, his voice rising merrily as he told of his carousing (though, as I say, now he was sober); but he gave me no chance to ask why he clutched the earth in his fear and cowered in the shadow of a tree.

Then once Master Lamb was a-bed, I recalled Lazenby, earlier in the summer, crying out about the bishop when I saw the fingers in the pool. And hadn't there been a darkness in the birches around the pool? A darkness that swam into my head, just as Master Lamb had described?

So I returned to the road and stared down its moonlit length, wondering if I dared once more cross in and out of the shadows of the trees to see who – or what – lingered among the branches.

A step sounded behind me, and I turned to find Lazenby, and I demanded what mischief he was up to, setting my heart thundering. But he had heard me putting Master Lamb to bed and had got up to help. But that was not why he had assailed me in the courtyard.

He said, "Come!" And his gaze was so stern that I followed him.

He would make two of me, Lazenby. And glad I was of his company as we walked through the herb garden in the moonlight, me, thinking again of the devil that Peggy saw.

I did not ask Lazenby where we were going. I assumed he had seen something between rising from his bed and finding me in the courtyard, for he is inquisitive like a cat is inquisitive, and he is not ashamed to look in windows. So I stayed silent, and followed him to the west side of the palace, moving under cover of trees and shrubs.

I was glad of that, for lights from the laboratory shone down on the lawn.

"Come," said Lazenby again, and we ran from cover, crouching low in the moonshadow of a cedar which towered but twenty paces from the laboratory windows.

We stopped under the tree and looked up, and I knew that Sir Martin at least, was there, for his voice fell harshly in the night air.

Then something touched my scalp; but it was only Lazenby in the tree, reaching down. In a moment I was beside him, and we clambered with much scuffing and shushing until we were level with the windows, then we crawled along a great branch, Lazenby at my back, for I understood he wished me to have the better view.

And I thanked God for the soft coarse bark under my hands, for I have never liked being higher than a horse's saddle; so I gripped the bark, pulling myself closer to these open windows, Lazenby occasionally holding my jerkin when I threatened to lean too far to one side.

Then I was close enough to see clearly into the room.

I must digress.

It may seem mysterious to talk now, of ghosts. But bear with me.

Many a tale is told in these parts, of spirits and demons. Aye, and by sober men and women. Especially around the ancient stones which stand not so many furlongs beyond the palace. You can imagine the discussions we have; but one point considered often, is why spirits do appear wearing their everyday clothes.

This is a fact. No one denies it – except those foolish enough to laugh at the very idea of ghosts. But none has explained how it is that clothes which lie rotting in a grave can manifest themselves around the spirit of the departed. Yet it is so.

Now.

I clung to the branch, with Lazenby behind me, and the open windows before me pouring light onto the lawn.

I saw Sir Martin Bentlock with his coat thrown aside, and his shaven head shining, for he was also without his wig. I saw Bishop Redman asleep on a trestle, wrapped in his black riding cloak, with his black boots gleaming, and his hair white as an angel's wing.

And I saw wonderful objects, but understood them not at all and therefore remember them but vaguely. But what I will never forget was the look on Sir Martin's face as he gazed upon the bishop.

Never have I seen such fury. Truly, he appeared

like a gargoyle, his bare scalp gleaming with sweat and his terrible features pulled out of human shape. Possibly I clutched the branch in my fear, making some small sound, for he stared, it seemed, straight at me; then I realized he could see little outside, looking from the brightly-lit room into the darkness. Then he leaned close over the bishop, listening, I thought, for breathing, and I feared the bishop was dead and not sleeping.

Then Sir Martin spoke. Quietly enough, though savagely; then louder as his rage loosened. "Wake up, man! Are you still there? An hour is gone. Has the ceremony freed you entirely from the flesh? You owe me too much! Awake, sir! My little knowledge added to yours has enabled your spirit to soar! Devil take you, sir, if you die!"

Here, Sir Martin turned to survey the room with its many candles, as if he expected not to be alone, though who could be there I had no knowledge – unless it was the Devil, whose name he used so carelessly.

He continued. "Come. Return. Return, I say. The demon is gone these many months. No one but the wench saw him in the herb garden. The others are fools who either believe too much, or believe nothing. There is no worry there."

Sir Martin scowled down on the bishop. "You *did* fox him? that brimstone-stinking demon! He *is* gone? We *are* safe from his demands? That is what you said when you invited me here! He gave you the final incantation that lets you live on – not merely free of your body – but after, when your bones be dust!

"Awake! Are you set to cheat me? I must know too! Shall I split your gizzard?!"

Here, Sir Martin paced up and down, his fists clenching and unclenching. Then he sat by the bishop.

"Forgive my temper," he growled. "Come. You do not wish to pass a thousand years alone? I would wait with you. You shall have the first suitable subject. Yes, yes! I know we gambled on it and you lost, but perhaps my hands dealt the cards stealthily. They know no honest way, now. You shall have the first child of true courage and return to live in his flesh.

"Perhaps it won't take a thousand years."

Sir Martin sat, panting.

His glance struck towards where I lay along the branch with Lazenby behind me, but he saw us not, and turned – scowling dreadfully – to the bishop.

And he spoke on at the bishop, cursing and raging, finally wiping his head with a kerchief. Then he approached the window and peered into the tree. I ducked my head to hide the paleness of my face which might be visible even in the dark. (I gripped the branch so fiercely that the following morning bruises darkened the backs of my hands.) But meantime, sweat ran under my shirt. I had no wish to face the wrath of Sir Martin Bentlock.

Then he hurried from the window. I felt Lazenby tug my ankle.

I glanced back and saw him point into the room, then vanish off the branch. I heard his feet strike the turf ten feet below. Inside the room, Sir Martin was lifting a candelabra and striding to the window.

In a moment he would thrust the candelabra into the night and send the candlelight through the leaves onto my sweating face. My fear of the height was nothing compared to my fear of being discovered by that human gargoyle, so I slid sideways off the branch, clinging for a moment to hang straight, then I dropped, and Lazenby's great hands caught my oxters and let me down gently, then he hauled me into the darkness beneath the laboratory windows.

"Is it you?" Sir Martin's voice scraped the night. "My Lord Bishop," he sneered, "it is not seemly to hang about in trees. What if one of your flock should see you? I know you are only a shadow, but your ability to appear in your natural form is most remarkable. No doubt with practice you will be able to manifest night or day, as you choose, with none to swear that you are not a real man, even though you be but a shade cast loose from your body."

Then the candlelight retreated into the room, and for the moment Lazenby and I saw no more; but I wondered at Sir Martin's words, for had Master Lamb not said – but an hour since – with words and gestures, that he had seen the bishop in a tree?

Then we heard the laboratory door close, and we sat, our backs to the cool stone of the palace wall, gasping our relief.

But our relief was short-lived.

Lazenby heard the sound first.

Footsteps on the grass.

Then the swaying light of a lantern approached from around the side of the palace.

We ran towards the cedar and hid behind its great trunk. The light bobbed towards us. We ran again, following the shadow of the tree into the darkness of shrubbery.

The light stopped under the cedar, and Sir Martin spoke up towards the branches, addressing the bishop. Then he stood as if undecided.

Was he mad? I wondered – to believe that the bishop was in the tree? The bishop lay on the trestle in the laboratory.

"So you're not there." Sir Martin spoke to himself. "Then where the devil are you? Not dead, I'll swear. Then wandering. But where? I must find him, for his body is cool. If he returns too late he will find it cold, and dead he will be, and nought gained, and my chance to join him in endless life, denied!

"I will not be denied! Think! He must be between the Druid's circle and the church. There is no energy beyond these points to hold him. But how do I search the two miles in the dark?

"He would not go to the circle for there is nothing between here and there but night, and he takes pleasure in terrifying any lone peasant for the delight of hearing him scream." Sir Martin chuckled. "As he did to that dolt and his friend at the well four weeks since! Ha! Ha! 'Pon seeing the groom's toes caught by roots, my lord bishop reached his hand out of the pool pretending to hold his foot – though he has no more substance than a stepmother's breath. No wonder the dolt fled! I believe I should have fled myself! Ha! Ha! Ha!

"So.

"Enough. My lord bishop will head for the town."

And Sir Martin ran, the lantern's light jerking his shadow monstrously across the lawn. And we followed, Lazenby and I, fearful of the terrible things we had heard, but more fearful of not learning what was to happen.

When we entered the road to the town, Sir Martin ceased running.

The shadows of the trees lay at a different angle from when I had rescued Master Lamb, for the moon had fallen down the sky. Sir Martin strode to an oak and addressed its branches. Lazenby and I lay in a ditch, and Lazenby shrugged with silent laughter. I hushed him angrily and demanded if he realized the meaning of what we had heard.

To my astonishment he replied, "Aye, Tom. My wits be not as quick as thine, but was my grandmother not drowned as a witch? Sir Martin and our bishop have called up a foul fiend. Yon Peggy Keller saw it and gave it to us feature by feature, just as my grandmother spoke of it. In return for payment it will tell secrets to those who ask the right questions."

I was truly astonished, for this part had escaped me. "Payment?" I asked.

"Hush! You speak too loud! Aye, payment. Some do trick the fiend out of payment, but he is cunning and patient. Patient, for he does not die!"

And I lay in the ditch, trembling suddenly, shocked at finding – it is shameful to confess this – but I was shocked that Lazenby should understand what I did not understand. And I trembled because I knew that what Peggy had seen in the herb garden was real, and that my lord bishop and Sir Martin had summoned the demon out of the Pit.

Then Lazenby roused me, and we followed Sir Martin's light along the road towards the town wall. And it was then I recalled that Master Lamb, earlier that night, had stared into the branches above him, saying, "I have seen the bishop! I have seen the bishop!"

For then I heard a voice whispering exactly these words.

Minutes before, I had lain trembling in the ditch.

Now I stood within the shadow of a tree, Lazenby beside me, the moon brightening the road, and shining on the thatch of the weavers' cottages which leaned on the town wall. And I trembled as with the ague, for never had I dreamed of such a voice.

Oh, a mere whisper it was, no more than a breath on a tongue, but I swear it was no human breath; and no human tongue.

Chills of deepest winter enclosed my flesh. Hair on my head rose in horripilation, and I may have fainted. For I found myself prone on the earthy road with Lazenby's hand over my mouth. And I felt him shudder.

Perhaps Sir Martin heard the words also, because though he was within the town gate, his lantern light paused, then raised itself, and I saw his face palely glowing. Then he returned with dreadful slowness, a dagger glinting in his hand.

Certainly, he was not seeking the bishop's shade, with the dagger.

I had no love of Sir Martin, but I could not allow him to walk towards the owner of that voice. I rose, and stood tall, hesitating. Should I call out? Or run to him?

But I did neither.

Sir Martin stopped outside the town gate a few paces from the end cottage. He moved the lantern, peering, and his shadow lay behind him, hiding from the light. And he turned as if he sensed the shadow's movement. His voice rasped, threateningly. Then the moon darkened, and I saw nothing but the yellow bobbing lantern, and perhaps two dots of light within the shadow, like a cat's eyes; then Sir Martin's raspings rose into a shriek that clenched my muscles onto their bones.

And the ultimate horror overcame me.

The lantern stopped bobbing. It froze in the darkness as if fixed to a house wall.

I counted heartbeats on the fingers of my left hand. I was counting on the fingers of my right, before the lantern dropped.

It toppled on the ground, but was not extinguished. Then in a frenzy, I ran forward and lifted the lantern. On the road lay Sir Martin's dagger. I swung the lantern around. I ran hither and thither. I dashed behind trees. I ran through the town gate, screaming Sir Martin's name. I ran along in front of the weavers' cottages. People appeared, bearing lamps and candles. We searched every corner.

No one in this world ever saw Sir Martin Bentlock again.

I don't recall the next hour clearly. I think Lazenby ran to the palace, for most of the household joined the search. What I do remember was the bishop, still in his cloak and black boots as I had seen him on the trestle in the laboratory, but walking now, his white hair shining amid the lights, like Hope in the darkness.

Lazenby told me later that the bishop – regarding

Lazenby as lowly as a sheep, without wit or voice – had murmured, "Now he has made payment." And the bishop's smile was aglow with kindness, but no kindness, Lazenby swears, lay in his heart.

That is Tom Keene's story, more or less as he told it to the notary almost two hundred years ago. The bishop died in 1803.

The palace was lived in by various successors, but, strangely, no one would stay more than a few months. It was said that the spirit of Bishop Redman haunted the palace, frequently seen, occasionally heard to speak "as if practising speech, like a man who has long been ill and must learn new use of his tongue" – to quote one witness. Inevitably, the palace fell into disuse and was demolished in 1830.

Andrew eased his legs.

He gazed into the fire's merry brightness.

Bishop Redman, Andrew decided, was still haunting the ley line.

The butcher had seen him in Knock Lane fifteen years ago. Andrew and Rosie had seen him today at the war memorial, then in the shopping arcade.

Something about electricity swam into Andrew's mind. Electric lights in the arcade had burst. Electricity was power. And the ley line was power. Could the ley line's power be some kind of electricity?

There was only one person to ask – Doctor John.

Andrew looked at the cover of the book. Maybe Doctor John would know also, what James had to do with all this.

"Huh!" said Andrew, and he smiled doubtfully at the fire. James's ghost, too, was walking the ley line, according to that loony youth.

Rosie sighed. She rolled over, Father's coat slipping from her back. Her eyes were open.

"Rosie?"

"Mmm."

"I know about the bishop."

"What?" Rosie stretched, her face scrunching prettily in the firelight.

"You wanted to find out about the bishop. He's in this book." Andrew flicked the book's pages.

From a back page, a square of paper slipped to the carpet. It lay flat, as if it had been rigid in the book for a long time. Which it must have been. No one but James could have put it there.

Andrew didn't lift the paper immediately. Rosie's eyes shut again. The fire splashed rich light around the hearth, touching Rosie's curls with gold. The square of paper seemed black.

Andrew leaned from his chair to pick the paper up. In the midst of its blackness, two silver dots caught the firelight. Andrew lifted the paper by a corner, and laid it on the book.

He shivered, withdrawing his fingers.

He was conscious of the fire hissing and snapping. The warmth of the bulb in the table lamp pressed his cheek. The darkness on the paper was black ink, stroked in fiercely as only James could do. The background of the drawing suggested trees and perhaps a structure, the straight lines reminding Andrew of the lychgate. In the foreground, taking up most of the page, was a figure, perhaps a little shorter than Andrew, but hideously shaped, and not human – never human! and so utterly repulsive that Andrew retreated into his chair leaving the paper on the book, on his knee, as far from himself as possible. The two dots were eyes marked in with metallic paint so that they glittered like moonlight.

Then Andrew peered closer.

His breath shook. It seemed that a north wind had found its way into the house and was easing its frozen body around his shoulders.

In a space at the foot of the drawing, James had printed four words in tiny lettering. And for the first time in his life, Andrew experienced true fear.

The words were: I HAVE SEEN THIS.

"Rosie."

"What?"

"Are you awake?"

"No."

"Yes, you are."

"Then why a–ask?" yawned Rosie from the rug. "And why are you sitting like that?" She pushed up onto one elbow. "You look as if you've a spider on your knee."

Andrew relaxed. "Sort of."

"What's the matter?"

"Will you stay here? I'm going to get Dad."

"What for?"

Andrew lifted the book with the drawing resting on it, and placed it beside the lamp. "I'll just be a minute."

He crossed the hall and opened the study door.

Father sat, like a black rock behind his desk, fist moving as he wrote swiftly, his lips rehearsing the sermon.

A gas fire in the fireplace pretended to be coal. The overhead light shone on shelves holding dark books, the books shining with gold lettering.

Andrew sat in a spoonback chair and slid his palms around the curving wood that framed the upholstery. He liked this room, with furniture handed down through the family.

"Dad," he said.

"Dad, is it?" said Father, his fist still wriggling. "Must be serious. Hold on." Wriggle. Stop. Father looked up.

"I want you to read something," said Andrew. "It'll take a little while."

"Worth interrupting my sermon for." It wasn't a question. "All right."

"It's in the sitting-room. Rosie's to read it too."

"Can we go then?"

Andrew didn't move. "I think it's about James."

"James," said Father. "That is serious."

"And other things."

"We'd better read it then. Before I grow too old."

Andrew led Father through the hall. Rosie was sitting on the rug at the fire hugging her knees. She looked up.

Father said, "We've to read something. Ah." He sat in the lamplight. He lifted the book from beside the lamp, letting the drawing slide off the page into shadow.

"I'll show you the chapter," said Andrew. He stared at the drawing. He didn't mention it. "Rosie, you read it too." And Rosie clambered onto the chair arm and followed Father's finger.

"It's about a ley line," she said, then crouched silently, her mouth open a little, reading.

Andrew sat on the rug.

"Uh," said Rosie, and Father turned the page.

Andrew waited.

Another page turned.

Father sighed.

Rosie frowned.

Andrew looked toward the windows. The trees in the front garden dressed themselves in black as the afternoon died.

More pages turned.

Andrew got up and went to the door. Rosie and Father made a cosy picture under the lamplight. Andrew walked into the kitchen.

He closed the door. "What's that smell? Are you baking!"

Mother beamed as she whisked something in a bowl.

Andrew looked into the bowl. "Chocolate sponge!"

"It's your favourite. Isn't it?"

"Yes. Of course. But you haven't baked for ages."

"I thought I should." Mother's glance wavered towards the window and the lychgate.

The sky stood pale above the dark garden.

"Shall I put on the light? Have you been crying?" asked Andrew.

Mother nodded, her hair hiding her face. She looked up at Andrew and smiled. "I'm trying to be brave. But I'm not. I've been reading magazines for a year. You and Rosie have..."

"We didn't mind helping. Not much."

Another smile.

"And your father's been so patient. I used to do things. For the church. Organizing things. At the university. I hadn't the heart." She spooned the mixture into a baking tray and spread it evenly. "I did so much baking!" She marched to the Rayburn, clanged open the oven door, sucked her burnt fingers, placed the baking tray in, banged the door shut with her toe. She began again with flour, butter, sugar, two eggs, cocoa. A whiff of salt.

"Another sponge?" said Andrew.

Mother shrugged. "Why not? I'm sure you can eat it."

"Yeh! Yes! And drop scones for supper!"

"I could do that!" agreed Mother. "I'll make the mix in a minute and leave it to stand until we're hungry again after tea. Tastes best that way."

"How can you remember recipes?" asked Andrew. "I can't remember a year ago. Not clearly."

"Some things you don't forget," said Mother, and worked hard suddenly, at the mixture.

Andrew knew that she was thinking of James.

"Was it very bad?" he asked.

"Was what very bad?" Mother held her head back, letting her hair fall away from her face. "I should have tied my hair up," she cried, as if wanting to change the subject. Then her hands rested on the rim of the mixing bowl. "Yes! It was bad! Finding James? That's what you mean? Oh, it was so bad! I did love him. And you. And Rosalind. But... He was the first, you see? My first baby. I loved you all equally. But you understand? The first is special. Just because he *was* the first. And he wasn't well.

"No one knew. No one who didn't need to know. James wouldn't hear of it. His heart wasn't strong. I need to sit."

Andrew slid a chair under her.

"He could have lived," sighed Mother. "A normal life. Taking proper exercise. Not overdoing things. I know he could! It makes you cruel. Doctor John said that. People who discover they have heart trouble change their personalities. Though James wasn't really cruel. He was just... Oh, I don't know. Just defending himself, I suppose, from his weakness. He loved you especially."

Mother sat hunched in the chair, her glance touching Andrew. "I know he bullied you. But you were his little brother. I think he would have died for you."

"Died for me?"

"Yes. He said as much." Mother's brow wrinkled. "Now what was he talking about? Fancy not remembering. He said it as if it was a certainty. You know. Not just that he would do it if necessary. But that he really would one day."

Flames roared gently in the Rayburn.

Andrew turned from his mother and stared at the window. He couldn't see the lychgate – not with the kitchen light on. He remembered Father saying that there is no greater love than dying willingly for someone else. Andrew hadn't really thought what

Father meant. Had he been talking about James?

Mother's chair scraped the floor as she stood up.

The whisk spun through the mixture. Andrew went close to her. The whisk stopped, filling the kitchen with the smell of chocolate; and silence. And flames murmuring.

"Tell me," said Andrew.

"Tell you?"

"About finding James."

"Well... It's so difficult. I don't want to cry again. I've cried too much over the months. I found him at the lychgate. An afternoon like this. Perhaps you remember? I don't know where you and Rosie were. Oh, at school. Of course. The lychgate light was on. I kept meaning to switch it off. I had baked a chocolate sponge. Oh, I think that's why I'm baking chocolate sponge today. James did enjoy it. He'd gone off with a slice. He was rather grey that day, which is why he wasn't at school. He was all right! It was just a precaution! He wasn't ill! He wasn't ill, Andrew.

"But he was busy. In his room. He came down. What a noise! Jumping the last steps. I could never prevent him doing that. Rushing through the kitchen. He stole ... snatched a slice of sponge and dashed out the back door. I remember his fingers were black with ink. He had been writing, he said, using his drawing ink. He said something strange. He paused after he lifted the sponge. He said, 'Tell little brother it's all for him.' I didn't know what he meant. I had the silly idea that he was talking about the sponge. Then he said – as if to explain, 'I'll die for him, Mum.'"

Mother sank again onto the chair.

"My head's thumping. Where's Rosie? Rosalind!"

"I'll do it," said Andrew, and put the kettle on.

He made tea.

Mother pushed the second tray of sponge mixture at him. He used a dish towel to open the door of the oven. Heat from the oven made him turn his face away. Then he sat with his mother, and they drank tea, and listened to the house.

5

Late Saturday afternoon.
Father walks in the garden; and
Doctor John hears a man screaming.

"There was something in his look," said Mother, "that made me wonder. When he spoke. With the chocolate sponge raised in his hand. It was his gesture. As if he had no intention of eating the cake. He took it because I expected him to. And his eyes were so excited and his skin so grey. He saw me notice his inky fingers, and gave a little shrug. Then he said what he said.

"The back door banged behind him. I remembered everything later. I wasn't really paying attention at the time. I was rolling pastry for a pie. The oven was still hot, you see. It's surprising what you can recall.

"Once, I went to the window, because I thought I heard James cry out. But the garden was dark and I couldn't see him, though the lychgate light was still on. And the cry could have been anything."

"What was he wearing?" asked Andrew.

"Wearing? Oh. I see. You mean Rosie's Hunter. Yes, he would have worn that if he was going any distance. No. Just his jumper I think. Most mothers would have noticed. 'Put on a jacket!' they'd have said. James was intelligent enough to know if he was cold. I sometimes wonder if I'm a proper mother."

Andrew smiled.

"Now I'm being silly again. Where was I? I heard James cry out. Or perhaps I didn't. Then I heard the lychgate crash shut. And I suppose I thought it was James returning from wherever, via the churchyard. Not falling against the gate. I hadn't asked where he was going, or how long he would be, or..."

"...if he'd changed his underwear."

Mother gasped a little laugh. "Yes," she said. "I finished filling the pie and laid the pastry over it. I put the pie in the oven. Then I realized that James was a long time coming in.

"I glanced out. I saw a dark shape on the ground under the light. It was difficult to make out, what with the shadow of the gate and branches moving. It seemed too large to be just James.

"Your father was out. I didn't panic. I walked to the door and opened it. I called, 'James!' then I walked down the path.

"Then I ran. I got so scared! '*James!*' Oh, I screamed! I screamed, for I knew it was him! And he was sprawled on his back, his mouth wide open, his eyes enormous. And I gathered him up. I carried him. I don't know how. God gave me strength. I carried him and laid him on the rug on this stone floor. I covered him with a coat from the hall because that was quickest. And I phoned Doctor John. But I knew James was dead. I held his hand. Sitting on the floor beside him. I closed his mouth and his eyes. Then his face relaxed until I almost couldn't recognize him. The smell of the warm pastry filled the kitchen. And cold air swirled in, because I'd left the back door open.

"I got up to shut the door. I couldn't help looking towards the lychgate. It was the only light apart from the sky. And in the shadow of the gate was a dark shape – like part of the shape I had seen when I first looked out. As if there had been two figures and one was still there, but small, like a monkey. Not a monkey. Like an ape. Isn't it silly? It was only the shadow of a branch, because the wind moved the branch, and the dark shape moved. And, of course, I'd seen nothing when I lifted James. Then it was gone.

"But. Something else. The pie in the oven. The smell of the pie. You know. So wholesome. And another smell. Like sulphur. Like rotten eggs. It came on the wind, as if carried from a neighbour's house. It hardly seems possible. Hardly seems sensible, even thinking about it. I suppose we latch on to silly things to keep our minds off our tragedy.

"I went into the garden. I did! I left my baby on the floor and went into the garden! Down the brick path. I stood under the lychgate light. There was no smell, except fresh air. I looked around. I wiped away my tears. I crouched, touching the grass where James had lain.

"I saw marks in the ground. The grass was wet with earlier rain, and muddy.

"Andrew, I could have sworn that a goat had been in our garden, leaving little cloven hoof prints. Do goats smell like sulphur?"

Andrew heard feet in the living-room, and Father's voice, slight with astonishment, "Do I smell chocolate sponge?"

The kitchen door swung in suspiciously, and Father's face crept round. Rosie stepped into the kitchen, one fist in her waist, mouth verging on a smile.

"Is it true?" challenged Rosie. "Mother? Have you made a sponge?"

Mother dabbed a tear from her cheek. "I'm good at sponges," she murmured slyly, and her wide-mouth gasp of laughter brought Father to her side. She stood up into his arms and laughed again.

"But you haven't baked since..." said Father.

"Since James died," said Mother. "You can say it. It's been a wasted year."

"A healing year," rumbled Father, not letting Mother go.

"You said things," sighed Mother, "which sank in slowly. Oh, I tried to ignore them. A newspaper blowing in a breeze. James's gravestone split. And then this morning..." Mother pushed from Father's grasp and embraced Rosie. "Rosalind, you must have been so frightened in the shopping arcade. Then all of you went silent."

"Did we?" said Father.

"*You* hid in the study. Rosie fell asleep. Andrew disappeared. And I thought, Where is my family? I'm sitting here in the kitchen reading the *Woman's Realm*, and you let me. As if reading magazines was important!

"Rosie was so afraid today! and she couldn't come to me for comfort. I haven't been a mother.

You dared not mention James in front of me. And I woke up today. That's how I felt. I woke up – from a nightmare of stillness and futility. And I want to say that I'm sorry." Mother held her face up to Father. He touched her cheek.

"I'm sorry," she said to Andrew and Rosie. And Rosie beamed, and Andrew looked at the oven wishing the cake was ready.

"Well," said Father.

He said, "Well," again, making Andrew look at him. "Let's sit down. Round the table." Father's mouth smiled.

"I'm done with crying," said Mother. "What's behind these strange happenings? You do *know!* Rosie, tell me again what you saw in the shopping arcade."

And Rosie, quietly, told her.

Then Andrew told her of their adventure with the youth.

"Did the verger," asked Mother, "find anything unusual at James's grave?"

Father shook his head. "But Andrew found out a lot about Bishop Redman from John Maydick's book."

"The bishop?" said Mother. "What does he have to do with James?"

"You know about him?" cried Rosie.

"Of course. He's supposed to haunt the town. The verger claims he wanders in and out the church looking very angry. But he doesn't like to mention it. Didn't they tell you about the bishop at school?"

"Fat chance!" said Rosie. "Anyway, not *everybody's* heard of him. The butcher in the arcade has seen him, but didn't know who he was."

"You worked that out?" said Andrew.

"Doctor John's book," sighed Rosie, "did suggest that something might be walking about that should've been dead years ago. I'm sure he meant the bishop."

Mother asked, "What does Bishop Redman have to do with the newspaper blowing through the churchyard? And what – may I ask! – does he have to do with James?!"

"Gently," said Father. "I'm not sure how it all comes together. But let's go through it." He took Mother's hand, and she smiled and nodded.

Father stared at the table-top as if he could read the facts of the last twenty-four hours on its wooden surface.

"I'm not sure how James fits in. But... Are you up to this, Mary?"

Another nod from Mother.

"This is the toughest bit for you. It is for me."

"I'm all right," whispered Mother, but her knuckles whitened around Father's hand.

"I don't think," said Father, "that James is Resting in Peace. I think," he continued quickly as Mother gasped, "that he is still here. I think James made the newspaper behave in that strange way to let us know he was around. Perhaps while he was gaining strength – trying to appear to us. Typical of him to frighten everybody out of their wits." Father's voice rose nervously. "I think James knew what was going on. He said to me – a few days before he died – he said that I was to remember this: He said that sacrifice was necessary in everyone's life. And that *he* would make the ultimate sacrifice – for Andrew!"

Then Father's head bent, and he did what neither Andrew nor Rosie had ever seen him do before – not even at James's funeral: he wept.

Then he recovered, and said, "I asked him to explain. But he laughed. He said, 'You'll find out, Dad.' Then he pushed me away, as if he were the adult and I was the youth. And I let him. He was so sure. I realized then that James knew more than I did about the spiritual life. Oh, he was *silly* in some ways! Of course! But youngsters frequently know more than adults about certain things. Don't they? How does Rosie know the things she knows? Female intuition! Whatever that means! And how does Andrew know how to behave the way he does?"

Andrew wondered what he did, that was different.

"You're afraid of nothing."

"Oh, Dad!" breathed Andrew.

"What I would give to be afraid of nothing! That is true faith. I think that's why James loved you so much. I think your lack of fear is the reason these things are happening. And if the groom in John Maydick's book was telling the truth – and I see no reason for him to have spent money recording the story with a notary if it were not the truth - then what I think happened is this: Bishop Redman wanted to live for ever. He experimented, and succeeded in freeing himself from his body while he was still alive. Which – by the way – is not as crazy as you might think, children. I'm told that people under anaesthetic frequently experience this.

"But the bishop discovered how to do it at will; then – with the help of..."

"Sir Martin Bentlock," said Andrew.

"...he discovered how to continue after death – which is different, of course, from leaving your body and going back to it.

"It was the bishop's intention to inhabit someone else's body. He needed – if I have understood John Maydick's book – he needed someone who was fearless."

"Fearless!" whispered Mother, and her startled glance landed on Andrew.

"The book doesn't say why. Presumably an ordinary chap wouldn't survive the change-over. Fear would overwhelm..." Father placed his hands flat on the table. "Anyway. Let's get on."

So they got on.

Father talking.

Andrew and Rosie adding their thoughts.

Mother asking questions; anxious, but nearly as sparkly as she used to be, before James's death.

And darkness settled over the town.

The wind blew rain into every corner.

Traffic faded. Few people moved on Main Street. A police car circled the square.

Nearer, in Broad Street, a youth huddled inside his leather jacket as he hurried away from the square. Rain chilled the back of his head. And he nodded like a horse, as he peered into dark doorways and avoided the spindly trees which quivered in the cold. He was walking towards the vicarage.

"The doctor's coming," said Father.

"Just now?" Mother stood up. "After tea would have done."

"As soon as I mentioned James," explained Father, "he said he'd come at once, and hung up. I didn't have time to suggest after tea."

"Maybe he smelt your chocolate sponge," said Rosie.

"The kitchen's a mess!" cried Mother.

"Sit down, Mary. Doctor John has been in the kitchen often enough. I know you've recovered your energy, but let's not shock the poor man."

"Oh, you!" smiled Mother, but she pottered quietly, and in five minutes the kitchen looked organized, if not exactly tidy.

"He'll be here soon." Father left the kitchen.

Andrew heard the front door open. Father's feet sounded on the doorstep, then crunched on the drive. Cold air sneaked in, and stole warmth from Andrew's legs.

Rosie shivered.

"Maybe he's been delayed," said Mother.

The front door shut.

Father came in rubbing his shoulders. "Cold wind. And rain. Let me near the Rayburn. No sign of the doctor."

"Did you go to the bottom of the drive?" asked Andrew.

"Mm. Hardly a soul about. Rain in the trees," said Father again.

"What did you see?" asked Rosie gently.

"What did I see?" Father turned his back on the kitchen, warming his hands. "Nothing much.

Street lights are on."

Rosie stared at Andrew. Andrew thought: she knows Father's hiding something. Mother filled the kettle and plugged it in. Then she noticed the silence. And became part of it.

They waited for Father to speak.

Mother sat at the table, her hands folded.

Father said, "Hah! That's better." And faced them.

He said, "What a lot of solemn countenances! Like a congregation on a wet Sunday." He beamed.

He sat down and drummed his fingers on the table.

He said, "Hmm," cheerfully.

Rosie went to him and caught hold of his ears. She pulled.

"All right!" said Father. "I'll talk! Mercy! You wouldn't hit a man with glasses?"

"You don't wear glasses."

"I never will if you pull my ears off."

"What did you see!" demanded Rosie.

"Oh, trees! And rain! Trees in the front garden! You know! And ... oh, something, something in the trees! Something pale if you must know! Moving! Dodging! Hiding! Rosie, I think your newspaper is back!"

"But you threw it in the bin!" said Andrew.

"Perhaps it's another one," said Father.

"Is this a joke?" demanded Rosie. She glanced at Mother.

"Not really," said Father. "There is something. Someone, perhaps. It's very dark among the trees. I only came in to get a heat and the torch. AND AN

ANORAK!" he yelled as Andrew ran to the cupboard under the stairs, Rosie pushing along beside him.

Father's fat anorak turned him into Supervicar, thought Andrew.

"Torch," said Supervicar, and led the way out the front door into the rain. "Your mother will be all right?" he asked.

"We're only in the garden," said Rosie.

"Should we spread out?" asked Andrew.

"If you like," said Supervicar, "but guess who's keeping the torch."

Andrew and Rosie followed Father among the trees.

Rain slanted down.

Drips hung in rows under branches. The wind whipped chillingly onto Andrew's cheek.

"What do we do if we find it?" hissed Rosie.

"It's only paper," said Andrew.

"*You* ran, last time!"

"So what? Follow Father, Rosie!" So they followed Father until they reached the garden wall, with the road beyond.

"Well," said Father. "Back we go. Hello? Did you hear something? Listen!"

Rosie huddled in the shelter of Father's bulk. She squiggled a smile at Andrew, and he thought again how attractive she must be to other boys, with her yellow curls, and blue-bright eyes.

He listened. "I heard a moan!"

"Over there!" said Rosie, and they plunged after Father, the torch turning the rain into a sparkling tunnel.

"There's something white!" cried Andrew. "Under that bush!"

"Not a newspaper," said Father, and marched forward.

"It's that horrible boy!" gasped Rosie.

"He looks ill," said Andrew, as the youth sprawled, soaking, his face quite as white as newspaper.

Father pushed the torch into Andrew's hand. "Up you come," he said, and lifted the boy clear of the ground. "Good thing the doctor's due."

"You knew it wasn't the newspaper," Rosie accused Father. "You're really a cruel person like James."

"As cruel as the Old Testament, I am," agreed Father. "Hold these twigs from his face. That's it. Onto the drive. Open the door somebody, let's get him warm."

Father headed into the kitchen. "Tea," he told Mother.

"Where did *he* come from?" cried Mother.

"Try to sit up. Close to the stove. Remove the jacket. Could you bring a blanket, Rosie? Andrew, get his shoes off."

"Trainers," said Andrew. "They're squelching. So are his jeans."

"Jeans off," ordered Father, and the boy, gasping, fumbled to loosen his belt.

"I brought two blankets," said Rosie. "Look at his skinny little legs. He really doesn't look well. What were you doing in our garden?"

"Nothing!"

"Nothing much," said Rosie.

"And the shirt," said Mother. "Drink this tea."

The boy gulped as Mother tipped tea into his mouth, for his arms were trapped in a blanket. She hung the shirt over the Rayburn.

The boy's lower lip unrolled then rolled up tight. "You going to call the police?"

"I don't think so," said Father. "Do you need them?"

"Don't tease him," said Mother. "Of course we won't. You haven't done anything, have you?"

"No."

"Why were you in our garden?" Mother looked at Rosie – though not for an answer to her question. Rather, as if Rosie *were* the answer.

"Under a rhododendron," observed Father.

"Like a fairy," murmured Rosie.

"I don't feel well!" moaned the boy.

"What's your name?" asked Father. "D'you have a phone at home? So we can phone your mother."

"Norrie. We ain't got a phone. I don't feel well!"

Mother's mouth opened as she lifted the thin jeans. Her head shook, but she said nothing, and Andrew smiled. Mother was hopeless at telling people what they should do.

"You're supposed to keep yourself warm in winter," said Andrew, and Mother looked at him from behind a curve of hair. "Saves you from catching flu."

"I ain't got flu."

"Certainly looks like flu," said Father.

"I ain't got flu. It's your fault I'm not well!" Norrie's face nodded around everyone in the kitchen.

"Our fault?" laughed Rosie.

But the horsy face nodded so full of fear that no one spoke.

"You lot," said Norrie. "You lot caused it. I don't know what you're up to, and I don't know how you done it, 'cos he's dead, that James. I know! But it's you and him! He done it! That James! That James of yours! He's the one who's killing me!"

Father stepped back as if the boy had struck him.

"That's a terrible thing to say!" shouted Rosie.

Mother fed Norrie more tea.

Father turned his back and removed his fat anorak. He vanished into the hall. He returned without the anorak, his face calm. "It's certainly a curious thing to say. You didn't mention this to my children this morning. When you followed them. When you pestered them in the tearoom."

"I wasn't pestering them! I wanted to talk!"

"You hurt my arm!" said Rosie, "and demanded a sausage roll!"

"I didn't mean it," mumbled Norrie. "I just wanted to talk. I wanted to tell you."

"Then why didn't you!"

"You didn't give me the chance! Throwing teacups! And that waitress'll get you! I heard!"

"Rosalind!" gasped Mother. "You didn't!"

"No, I didn't!"

"Only because he stopped her!" Norrie glowered at Andrew.

Andrew said, "You started it. So don't blame Rosie! You said terrible things. Just like you're doing now! Why don't you talk sensibly! You don't know how, do you? All you can do is annoy people because you can't hold a decent conversation! Don't you accuse us of anything! Why were you following us? What were you up to in our garden?"

"Andrew," said Father. "That'll do. I expect you're quite right, but give Norrie a chance to answer your questions."

Norrie reached out from his blanket and lifted his tea. He drank.

"More?" asked Mother.

Nod.

"Try to tell us," said Father, "what you know." He frowned. "I wonder where Doctor John is."

Norrie scowled at the floor, nursing his cup. Rosie took off her Hunter. Andrew gave her his anorak; she gave him a look, but went into the hall. The door to the cupboard under the stairs opened and shut.

Rosie came in and leaned on Andrew's shoulder as he sat at the table. Andrew wiggled his toes inside his wellingtons.

"*You* know," said Norrie. He flickered a glance at each of them. Mother busied herself at the toaster while she listened.

"Things," mumbled Norrie, and Rosie leaned despairingly on Andrew, then sat down.

"Take your time," said Father, and sent his tiniest wink to Andrew.

"I didn't know him. Your James. Not really. He was always in the top class at school. No time for the likes of me!"

Rosie's lip crinkled and the horsy nod dipped low.

"He gave me a telling-off once. Years ago. I

didn't *do* anything! Well, you know! Hardly touched you." His head bobbed at Andrew, and Andrew drew in a breath of realization.

"You're Norman!" he said, flashing a glance at Rosie. "I don't remember you, but Rosie told me—"

"I didn't do nothing! But your James got onto me about it. He scared me. He said things. What would happen if I touched you again. My dad said to cuff him, but I daren't, 'cos of the way he looked at me, and somebody said he wasn't well enough to get hit. So I didn't. And he didn't say nothing else. Not for ages. Years, I mean.

"I watched him. He got quiet. Like he really wasn't well; with something bothering him. You know. Like he was worried, but excited too.

"I seen it in him. I'm not stupid! I seen him in the playground, looking around as if his mates was coming. But it weren't his mates he wanted.

"He would stare, and I knew he'd spotted who 'e was looking for, but I couldn't tell who. All I saw was kids. I thought once there was a man, standing in a shadow, but he weren't real. An old chap, all in black. But I didn't see him!"

Toast popped up in the toaster. Mother scraped quietly with butter; she chopped cheese. Norrie's lip rolled and unrolled.

"Ta."

Andrew noticed Rosie glancing at the ceiling. He looked up, but saw nothing unusual.

"Things," said the youth, "happened. Sort of. You know. He'd be talking to me, your James, then he'd be gone.

"Then I'd see 'im across the playground with his mates, and I couldn't remember him going.

"Or he'd be at me, the way he does – the way he did – then I'd be'n my class, half way through some stupid lesson, an' the last thing I'd remember is James's voice.

"He scared me. I was glad when he died. Sorry missus, but he's sucking the life out of me. I thought it would stop with 'im dying. Then I thought he had a twin brother, though I knew he hadn't. I *really* saw 'im today! And I said it, didn't I? He's got a twin brother! I asked you two, didn't I?

"But it wasn't his twin brother leaning on your shoulders. I knew that. He was there, real as could be. Only it was me keeping him alive – if he is alive. That's wot it was all about, I reckon. He was taking something from me before he died. I don't know what. And he keeps taking it. Like a vampire in them old films. Not biting my neck – I don't mean that! But sucking the life out of me. This ain't flu, you know, though I'm shivering. Can I 'ave another bit of toast?"

Father's mouth closed.

Then he whispered, "This is terrible. Are you saying that my son is haunting you?"

Nod.

"To keep himself in this world?"

"I reckon. Can I have a bit more cheese, missus? Ta."

"To what purpose?" said Father, staring hard at the table-top.

"Something about the old chap in black," said Norman. "Though I never saw *him*. Not proper. I ain't sure about him. But I was always seeing a dark patch. A... I don't know how to say it. Like something was keeping the daylight off your James. But just sometimes. An' it made me think of that old chap. I dunno why. My dad took me to Doctor Maydick—"

"Yes, where is Maydick?" muttered Father.

" —cos he said I wasn't right in the head. But I was. But I kept disappearing. Not disappearing. Not me. But I'd be one place one minute, then somewhere else later, and not knowing how I got there. Same as when James was alive. I don't see James, or nothing. 'Cept today. I don't hear him. But it is 'im. Taking away my thoughts. And I'm always tired after it. Dead beat. Sucking the life out of me. So's he can stick around. So's he can *do* something, I reckon. I don't feel well."

"So that he can do what?" demanded Father. But he was speaking to himself, and no one replied.

"Your colour's better," Mother told Norrie.

Rosie's glance wandered again to the ceiling, and her lips parted, but she relaxed back into the silence.

She knows something, thought Andrew, and watched his sister.

Rosie sat, just her eyes searching, as if something were seeping down into the kitchen. Then she looked full at Andrew. She said, "Daddy!" and Father jumped.

Rosie's blue stare burned into Andrew.

"It's happening!" she said. "The darkness is gathering!"

Outside, the wind tried to drag tiles from the vicarage roof; it thrashed the trees in the front garden, and moaned in the churchyard.

Two miles away, the same wind pulled clouds over the stone circle, spraying rain through the headlights of a car parked on the wild grass. The clouds spilled lightning, making Doctor John look up from where he stood in the centre of the circle.

Then he crouched, and ignoring the rain dashing at his yellow waterproofs, pulled from his pocket, a chestnut.

A string unravelled, and the chestnut dangled. He steadied the chestnut against the wind, but it swung and bobbed. The doctor crinkled his eyes, letting his mind sit blank.

The chestnut seemed to push into the wind, but the wind resisted. The nut pushed harder, circling reluctantly on its string. The doctor felt no surprise.

He sat, empty-minded, his eyes observing the quicker swing of the chestnut.

Rain rattled on his sou'wester.

Water soaked up into his shoes.

Then alarm nudged his mind, for the string blurred with speed.

The chestnut whirled until the string spun flat out.

The doctor frowned. The string broke, releasing the chestnut, which flew with the wind, vanishing into the rain and the furious grass.

For a moment the doctor remained crouching. Never had he seen such energy, though he knew that the ley line was most active at this time of year.

Then the fear that had been with him since James

first spoke of the bishop – almost two years ago now – reared up in his mind, and he ran to the car. He hadn't thought – when the Reverend Ainsley phoned – that so much power could be moving in the ley line. He hoped desperately that he had not wasted time coming to the stone circle to check the energy level at its source.

A suitcase, covered in raindropped dust, was strapped into the passenger seat. The Rover's engine still murmured, for the doctor had not turned off the ignition.

The car hurtled over the turf, lurching towards the road. The tyres screamed as they touched tarmac, and Doctor John was heaved forward from thirty miles an hour to fifty. There was little traffic. He went through the Bishop's Gate at seventy. He approached the square at ninety, and braked as the police car returned on its patrol. He flashed his lights at the police, knowing they would recognize his car, and he saw, through his rear window, smoke pouring from his tyres as he skidded out the other side of the square. He was touching ninety-five when he reached the vicarage.

The car crashed through the drive's gravel and slid sideways towards the trees. It stopped beside a tree with just enough room for the doctor to open his door.

He stared.

Every light in the house blazed into the rain, and above the groan of the wind, a man was screaming.

6

Saturday evening.
Doctor John sets a trap;
and Andrew runs away.

"The darkness is gathering!" Rosie's blue glance shifted from Andrew's face, to above his head.

Norrie gaped. Mother stared up.

Father said, "I see it. A good cure for darkness is more light. Switch on the strip lights." And Rosie switched on the lights which hid under the wall cupboards to illuminate Mother's worktops.

"Andrew. Come with me. You three stay here. Prayers wouldn't go wrong."

Andrew was pushed into the hall. "Lights on," said Father.

Andrew went into the sitting-room. He clicked on the overhead light. The table lamp was still lit. He switched on the wall lights, then went upstairs to James's room, Rosie's bedroom, and his own bedroom. He made a smile for Father as they met on the landing and trundled down the stairs.

"Look," said Andrew.

"What? James's painting? What about it?"

"Every time I go past, it's moved. I thought it was just me bumping on the stairs."

"It's certainly hanging at a strange angle. Maybe you nudged it on your way up. Does this matter, Andrew? I think the lights are helping a little, but I'm getting nervous. Is the darkness all through the house? I'm not even sure I believe that the old bishop is floating around. Maybe there's something wrong with our eyes. Poisoned by your mother's coffee," he concluded gloomily.

"I think it's just James," said Andrew, straightening the picture. "Letting us know he's here. That he's always been here." Andrew ignored Father's startled glance, and headed for the kitchen.

An image of James's churned grave jumped into Andrew's mind. He saw again where the lightning had run through the grass, and the green stain on the church tower wall around the lightning conductor. He looked back up the staircase. James's picture again hung at an angle.

Father urged Andrew into the kitchen.

Darkness stood amid the light; like black curtains so fine you could only see them from the corner of your eye.

"How very odd," stated Father.

"What do we do?" asked Rosie.

Father sat down suddenly but said nothing. Norrie, Mother and Rosie waited.

"Don't you know?" whispered Rosie.

"Huh!" said Father. "You'd think so, wouldn't you? Vicar of this parish and several others for nineteen years, and can't yet deal with the dead. There *is* a ceremony of exorcism, but I don't have it by heart. I could look it up. But would it work on someone who is *deliberately* a ghost? I admit that I really have no idea what to do! And it frightens me. Listen to that rain."

They listened to the rain rattling on the kitchen window. They listened to the wind sighing around the stone corners of the house.

Father said, "I'd better try."

He went out, and returned, fumbling through a leather-bound volume.

He sat blinking at the pages. "I can't see it." He pushed the volume at Mother. "Can you read that?"

Mother gazed at the book. She said, "Um..."

"Let me look," said Andrew; but darkness hung between him and the pages, and, really, it didn't matter.

Nothing much mattered. Just sitting was fine. Looking at Norman, his head horsing up and down, ready to doze; Rosie, with a slice of toast forgotten in her hand; and Father, puzzled but unworried by the gloom which overhung the kitchen.

Maybe dozing was a good idea.

Did the darkness have arms? Andrew sensed arms reaching down, like a gigantic friendly spider, its many limbs drifting closer. Soon, sleep would soften away his problems. James wasn't helping. He was just a sadistic youth who had died of a weak heart...

Andrew's head wobbled. A hand was rough on his shoulder. Who was shouting? Was it Father? He must have really stirred himself to make such an effort. I expect he prayed, thought Andrew.

Then thoughts which were not Andrew's edged into his brain; as if someone old and brittle-minded had dipped their head into his. Certainly not Father's thoughts.

A sound reached Andrew; like a book placed to his temple then the book slapped. He realized that a hand had struck his cheek, trying to waken him, but the sensation hit him from a distance; like Rosie rushing from a distance in the arcade...

The grip on Andrew's shoulder felt large and strong. Was he on his feet? Had Father lifted him?

Something bumped painfully across Andrew's chest. The inside of the kitchen sink loomed at his face.

The image of the sink melted, like wax softened with hot water. Though – Andrew decided – the water was cold. He could feel it in his hair; running onto the backs of his ears; blurring his eyes and his view of the sink.

He jerked his head up, and pain struck the back of his scalp. He knew he had hit himself on the tap.

He grasped the edge of the sink, which pressed into his chest. Then Father's church-filling voice reached him; a wordless scream that drove the dream-state from Andrew's consciousness; and gasping, he clung to Father, mumbling, "I'm all right!"

"I thought I'd lost you!"

The doorbell rang, and a thundering of fists-on-timber filled the hall.

Andrew used his sleeve to scrub water from his face. He winced at his slapped cheek. "Doctor John!" he panted. The darkness had retreated.

Rosie ran. The front door let in cold air; and Doctor John's voice.

The doctor lumbered into the kitchen. He dropped a suitcase at Rosie's toes, "Open it, Rosie!" and threw his yellow waterproof and sou'wester into a corner. "Someone was screaming?" He stared at Father, who nodded.

Doctor John snatched a pair of rubber boots from the opened case. "You fought him off then? The bishop? I gathered from our word or two on the phone that you've read my book. Good, good!" The doctor's shoes landed on his waterproof. He pulled on the boots, and turned around as if admiring the kitchen. He always reminded Andrew of a blue suit full of sausage. "The energy in this place! It's devastating! I don't need my chestnut to tell me that!"

"Chestnut?" said Mother.

"Hello, Mary. Yes. I use it for dowsing. Tell you later. Seen James?"

Doctor John's eyebrows encouraged an answer. But –

"Right. Silly question. I thought you might know that James was still—"

"Norrie has seen him," said Father.

"Norrie? Oh, Norman. Hello, Norman.

"I've been keeping an eye on our Norman," prattled the doctor. "Professionally, he has a virus. In fact, James is draining him rather more than I like. Norman also – fortunately – really *has* a virus, so I'm not recording lies. You're looking better, Mary," he told Mother. "Is she better?"

"Yes—" said Father.

"Pass me that towel," said the doctor. "Shift those dishes." He pushed dishes from the centre of the table. "Take them right away, please." The doctor dried rainwater from his hands. "Rosie, pass me the rubber mat from the suitcase." He threw the towel at Mother and flapped the mat over the table. The mat hung all round the table almost to the floor. "Give me your shoulder," the doctor instructed Father, and he leaned on Father and stepped hugely onto the table. "Switch off the centre light, somebody."

He filled one hand with the towel and removed the light bulb.

"Now pass me up the suitcase. Careful, Rosie! Dry the rain off it with the towel… The towel, Mary! Right, up it comes! Catch the newspaper as I pass it down!"

Layers of fine wire unfolded from the case.

Newspaper, separating each layer, fell into Rosie's arms. Andrew found the suitcase thrust against his chest.

The doctor grasped a bayonet plug connected to the wires, and pushed it into the light socket.

"Everybody help. Tease out these wires. They're in the shape of a net. Take it over my head. Spread it down around the table. See that black box near the socket? Transformer. That means we get high voltage but low current. When we switch on you'll go up in a blue light, but it won't do you any harm – so long as you've got your wellies on. But it plays the devil with spooks! You can put the suitcase down, Andrew.

"The bishop," explained Doctor John, without noticing the open mouths of his audience, "needs the special power of the ley line, to sustain his beastly existence. That's because he's not a real ghost – the way any decent person would be.

"He's arranged things so that he can possess someone else and live in their body. A real ghost couldn't do that, being on a different plane from us.

"The bishop is still on this plane, existing in a subtle electric body. He can top up the ley power, with power from any electric system. Do you know that the ironmonger in town sells eight times as many light bulbs as his rival in Warwick? Nobody knows why. Except us. But the bishop can't leave the ley line. He'd fizzle out – unless he succeeds in taking over someone else; then, of course, he can go anywhere. But if he touches this little lot –" the doctor waved at the net, which now surrounded him as he stood bent on the table, " – he'll end up where he belongs – which is far away from here! Everybody understand? Not a clue? Never mind.

"All we have to do is lure him here – to the kitchen – which is easy. Andrew sits inside the net, and when the bishop touches the wires, *fizzle!* He's had it. Gone. Deceased. The bishop, I mean, not Andrew. Switch on!"

"Are you sure it's safe?" asked Rosie.

"Switch on," said Doctor John, and Rosie switched on.

Nothing happened.

The doctor touched the wires, and blue light flared alarmingly and sparks fell to the floor. He slid off the table, his back alive with electricity. He ducked under the net, and stood clear. He pushed at his hair.

"Makes your curls stand on end. Smells funny, too. Andrew? You've got your wellies on. Wellies and the rubber mat will insulate you. Want to pop in?"

"How will the net stop him?" asked Andrew. "If he feeds on electricity?" He really did not want to sit inside the doctor's cage.

"See the transformer? It's also a DC converter. Direct current instead of the usual alternating current. Like a little bolt of lightning. Poor old Redman is in for a nasty shock – literally."

"What about us?" said Father, his gesture enclosing Mother, Rosie and Norman.

"He's not after us," said the doctor. "We're not bally-well good enough. Don't be alarmed!" But Andrew wasn't alarmed at the blue flare exploding on his body as he crept under the net. His hair prickled and Rosie laughed. Doctor John grinned.

Andrew pushed his hair flat. "I feel like a monkey in the zoo," he said. "How long do I have to sit here?"

"Blessed if I know!" said Doctor John. He frowned at Mother gathering the newspaper which had separated the wires of the cage.

"You don't need this?" said Mother.

"No. Not at all."

Mother fed the paper to the pedal bin.

"No," repeated Doctor John quietly. "We won't need that. We constructed the cage more than a year ago – James and me. Yes! Yes! We knew then that the bishop wanted to possess someone! My researches for the book told us that! You do know about the book? Yes, you did say. Well, James took things a step further and went..."

Doctor John hesitated. Then he dashed to his waterproofs and lifted them. He stood his shoes in the corner like an invisible dunce. He hung the waterproofs on a hook behind the door. "I forget I'm not at home."

Mother said, "Tell us what James did."

The doctor rubbed rainwater from his hands. "James went looking for the bishop. Typical! I was the author of the book – but it's James who looks for the ghost. I never thought of it.

"Not that I had the time. And a doctor must tread carefully, as it were! Ghost-hunting! Couldn't risk it locally. I'd have no patients! I think the book's sensible enough. Nobody's complained about that..."

"You could do with some tea," said Mother.

"Thanks! I was scared I'd be too late getting here!" The doctor's voice rang over the clang of the kettle. "But the energy originates at the stone circle so—"

"The bishop will come back?"

"Rosie? Yes! He'll come back. Gathering steam, I guess. But Andrew's safe. Don't worry."

Andrew dabbed a finger at the net and watched sparks showering. "Did James find the bishop?" he asked.

"Yes, indeed. Oh, let me help." The doctor caught Norrie's blankets, as Mother handed the youth his stiffening jeans.

"They're not really dry enough," said Mother. "Let me hang them up again."

"No socks?" commented Doctor John. "Your toes can develop fungus..."

Andrew looked at Father. Father's mouth lifted. He knew that Doctor John was avoiding talking about James.

Andrew slid out from under the net. Everyone moved back from the sparking blue fire.

Andrew shared Rosie's chair, and said, "Tell us what James found out, Doctor John. Mother can take it. We all want to know. Really, we do."

Doctor John paced across the kitchen. He frowned at his waterproofs on the hook, and returned to his tea. He gulped half the cupful.

"Right," he said. "Right, right." But he frowned again, as if the tea was offensive.

"I couldn't put any of this in the book," he said. "It was James's doing, not mine. And the book wasn't about just the bishop. And as I said, being a doctor, I must take care what I publish—"

"Do tell us!" said Mother.

"Yes. Good tea. Could you scrape up a slice of that toast for me, Mary? I don't remember eating today. James found the bishop in various places – because he was looking for him, y'understand.

"If you weren't looking, you might see him and not notice anything odd. He's so real some of the time. But James had dug up portraits of him, and read reports of sightings. You know – elderly clergyman walks through wall, and stuff like that. But James cornered him a few times. James was like Andrew to some extent – not as scared as you might expect.

"We thought maybe it was him the bishop would be after. But it was Andrew. Andrew being even less scared, and, of course, more healthy—"

"He's been spying on me?!" demanded Andrew.

"Oh, not too closely! Don't worry. Because he could be seen – some of the time. Or his darkness would frighten people. And if there wasn't enough power in the ley line, he would just exist, practically invisible, until the power built up. Isn't it crazy? James sitting in a corner of the church, chatting to a dead man? Or finding him in the town!

"That was tricky. The old boy could fool your eyes, so that you weren't sure you *were* seeing him! And if the light was wrong, one person would see him and others couldn't – depending on where you were standing. He could even blot out real people, apparently."

Rosie's head turned, her face close to Andrew, and she mouthed, "War memorial." Andrew nodded. Norrie hadn't seen the bishop at the war memorial; and they hadn't seen Norrie.

"The thing was," continued Doctor John, and his sausage limbs moved as if he couldn't believe his own words and was trying to wave them away, "everything that the groom said – you read his story in my book – was confirmed by the bishop. Oh, I feel stupid even saying it out loud!"

"Go on!" urged Father.

"Go on," sighed Doctor John. "I'll go on. The bishop talked. He talked and talked, quite clearly it seemed, but with quaint sayings, and some odd pronunciation. How he talked! And James tried to persuade him not to go on with his scheme – but his will was iron-fast! He had waited all this time! Two hundred years, you know! He wasn't going to give up now! Not when a child like Andrew was available to be taken over! Not after summoning a demon from the Pit and sacrificing poor Sir Martin Bentlock in return for knowledge! He *would* continue! And he threatened James with hell-fire for his impudence.

"But he didn't know James. James could talk too. James could persuade! Didn't he persuade Norman to give up part of his electrical essence? leaving him like a zombie for minutes on end!

"And Bishop Redman in his lust for talk, and with James on at him, released one or two – oh, maybe two or three little gems. Gems of knowledge that would let James leave this world, yet remain part of it. Remain. To help Andrew..."

The doctor's voice faded, then sang in his throat, soft as the murmuring flames in the stove. "For James knew that his own life would not be a long one – not with his weak heart... So he thought it worthwhile to sacrifice what years – perhaps, what decades – he had left, and use that knowledge, so foolishly given by the bishop, to summon – yes, to summon – I hate to say it... but, to summon – for himself – the demon."

The wind sighed beyond the kitchen window.

The stove grumbled.

Andrew stood up and touched the wires. Sparks scattered, making everyone jump.

"Sorry," he whispered. Then he remembered. "Wait a minute!"

He darted through to the sitting-room. Cautiously he lifted James's drawing of the demon from where it still lay by the lamp. He carried it to the kitchen and placed it on Father's knee. He told Father, "It was in the book."

Everyone stared at the drawing. Father didn't touch it. His mouth opened. His voice shook.

"It's revolting!" he gasped. He stood up, letting the drawing flutter to the floor. "Excuse me! I'm being silly. It's only a sketch. By my son."

He lifted the drawing and read, "'*I have seen this*'." His shocked gaze drifted to Mother. "He saw this? Our James saw this! He summoned it out of Hell?"

The paper shook in Father's grasp. Mother hurried to him. "Sit down," she said. "He did it for Andrew."

"Oh, Mary!"

"He did it for Andrew, dear. Yes, it's terrible –" She took the drawing and looked at it. "Very, very terrible." She passed it to Doctor John who held it by its top corner; Rosie and Norman crowded to see it. Mother said, "But he met this creature—"

"Oh, not a creature, Mary!" whispered Father. "Not a created being! A negative monster! And James – !" Father's cheeks sagged in horror.

"James faced it," declared Mother, and Andrew watched as her words reached Father; and Father relaxed, colour returning under his skin.

He nodded.

"Thank you, Mary."

Father sat again, Mother kneeling, holding him, as she had held Andrew, like a child, saying nothing more.

"There's something on the back," said Rosie.

Doctor John turned the drawing. Andrew saw a

mass of James's fine printing.

"Read it out," said Mother, and Father nodded.

"Yes." Doctor John hunched his limbs. His glance darted to the corners of the kitchen. Then he scanned the paper.

"Terribly childish," he said. "Amazing how intelligence and silliness can live together in one head. James must have been near panicking to write like this. Oh, God! Poor James! I can't read it aloud!"

He offered the page tremblingly.

Andrew snatched it, and slowly read out the tiny black print:

"Ho! Ho! Ho! As Father Christmas would say!!! Arf! Arf! even! Who would believe how easy-as-peasy-pie it is to conjure demons!!!! Nobody realizes that they want to come here! Hard luck, they stink like hydrogen sulphide multiplied to the tenth factor!!!!! Though when the brute was gone, its pong faded fast. Dad wouldn't've been too jolly pleased with brimstone stenching up the old vicarage. Bad for custom! Sorry, Dad! Hope you know what I'm on about by the time you read this. If you read it. Probably doesn't matter.

I'm sure the Bish is losing his marbles. Two hundred years of floating around this dump would drive anybody potty! Poor old sod was trying to be cunning, giving me the incantation! So that I would be dragged down to hell instead of him. He couldn't have fooled a half-wit with his crazy smiles. He was trying to talk like a sixties hippy. He looks amazingly real. Better than a hologram! Walks around like the genuine whatsit, though he can fade and reappear elsewhere. Saw him do this. Trying to frighten me. tried to make me think I'd die if I saw his face! That's his idea of entertainment. But he doesn't reckon with the ainsley spirit. Does he Dad?!!! Always quoting the bible, he is, but he's forgotten, greater love hath no man than this: that a man should lay down his life willingly for another. Or something like that. Since that's wot I'm doing, this ere demon ain't got a chance, pardner, of dragging this Ainsley anyplace!

But I've got to go through with it because the old devil has a few tricks up his spooky sleeve yet! (I mean the Bish, of course!) So I must pop off and keep an eye on little brother until the bish gives up (which he could do, I think, being potty – or he might even forget!!!!) My method is simple. I've been working on that idiot in the dummies' class, Norman somebody. I don't even know his last name! But he's so dim I can talk him into anything. I suppose I'm hypnotizing the poor chump, but he's got lots of the psycho-electric energy I need, and with the hints the bish gave me and an idea or two from some of my books, I really think I'm on Norman's wavelength. The bish used the odd peasant, apparently, in the old days, as an extra energy source, until electricity became available. Me, I'll stick to Norman. Can't risk fizzling out by soaking up the wrong electric current. Don't know enough about it. And I've a lot of catching up to do as far as putting in an appearance goes! I guess me and the bish will reach Zenith at the same moment – that is when the old ley line is pouring out power! Norman will be OK eventually, I guess. But what a crud! Sorry Norm! Sorry, again Dad! Shouldn't speak ill of the daft. I did the drawing on the back of this page, last night. Doing that helps me face that little horror again. I'm to meet it at the lychgate tonight. Putting on a big smile for Mum.

SHE'S IN THE KITCHEN. CHOCOLATE SPONGE, IF MY NOSE TELLS ME RIGHT. MY APOLOGIES MUM, FOR DOING THIS TO YOU, BUT I KNOW YOU'LL UNDERSTAND. YOU'RE THE BEST MOTHER ANY YOUNG SUPER-HERO COULD HAVE. LOVE TO YOU AND DAD AND LITTLE ROSIE AND LITTLER ANDREW. I CAN'T PUT IT OFF ANY LONGER. YAHOOOO!!!!"

Mother sobbed.

Father sat, grim and pale.

Doctor John took the page from Andrew and gazed at the words as if they might change, and bring good news.

Norman's lip rolled and unrolled.

"Oh, dear God!" whispered Father.

Andrew had never really believed that James had loved him. But now…

He sat close to Rosie, and when she hugged him, her motherliness overwhelmed him, and he wept.

"What can we do!" gasped Rosie.

Doctor John sighed, but didn't answer.

Andrew knew that there was no answer. Unless James came up with something.

He looked at the wire cage. Would the bishop be potty enough – James's word! – to touch the wires?

Doctor John looked at the ceiling.

"Is it getting darker?" asked Andrew. He wiped his eyes.

"I think you should pop into the cage," whispered Doctor John.

Andrew handed James's drawing to Father, and reluctantly – almost not noticing the blue flares – lifted the skirt of the cage and stood up inside, then clambered onto the table.

Mother reached for him, but Doctor John put his hand on her arm. "It's time," he said. Then his head jerked, and everyone heard him draw in a breath of horror.

In a corner of the kitchen where the darkness had gathered thickest, stood the old man Andrew and Rosie had seen at the war memorial. He was taller than Andrew expected, strongly built and quite as real as Mother, who rose to face him.

"*Hi, everybody!*"

Andrew's muscles hauled his body into a crouch. His heart heaved, thrusting blood through his limbs.

The bishop stepped forward. Light shone on his white hair – but dimly – for the darkness stood between the bishop and Andrew's eyes.

Rosie was bending forward as if to see better.

"IN THE NAME OF OUR LORD, JESUS CHRIST," boomed Father, "WHO HAS ALL POWER OVER DEMONS AND SPIRITS, I COMMAND THEE, DEPART TO THINE OWN PLACE, NEVER TO RETURN!"

Father's voice shook the air in the kitchen.

The bishop eased his head forward, wicked as a tortoise. And his smile spread radiantly, so that Father glanced at Mother in confusion. But Mother shook her head fiercely; and Father stepped forward, and boomed again, ordering the old man to depart.

"*No,*" said the Bishop, and he was suddenly past Father.

Rosie screamed and darted to Mother. The Doctor lumbered between the bishop and the cage.

But the old man stood close to the wires; and Doctor John turned, startled, for no one had seen the bishop move.

Behind him, Father caught Doctor John's shoulder. The doctor stood very still.

Andrew gaped at the eyes above the bishop's smile, and shuddered – for only emptiness looked back at him.

Andrew edged away within the cage, until one rubber-booted foot dipped over the table's edge, touching the wires, jangling them, but no sparks leapt. Which was correct, Andrew decided.

Then the bishop walked – peering in his gentle fashion – around the table, Andrew turning to face him, watching the smile dying, then beaming suddenly.

And one of the strip lights which lit the worktop turned black. Another strip light flickered. Darkness arose in the kitchen. More lights died. The bishop smiled up at Andrew on the table, but his glance went higher. Andrew touched the wires of the cage, but no flare lit the darkening room. Which was not correct. The power of the cage was gone.

"NO-O!" boomed Father. And the bishop hesitated.

Andrew slid out under the cage and fled to the back door.

Screams and voices followed him down the brick path.

The wind sighed, shaking the trees, then trailed into silence.

Rain thrummed straight onto the grass. It beat onto Andrew's head.

The back door banged shut, cutting off the glow from the kitchen. They're trying to keep the bishop in, thought Andrew.

Father's great voice soared mightily with the Lord's Prayer.

Darkness smothered Andrew. The path scraped under his feet, guiding him towards the lychgate.

Lightning stroked the sky, brightening the graveyard. Andrew found the latch and opened the gate.

Thunder whispered.

He looked back at the house. The light which filled the windows, somehow, did not escape into the garden.

Father's voice bellowed a vast, lung-bursting "AMEN!"

Then lightning struck again, silently amid the rain – and on the path, near the shut back door, a pale thing swayed; and Andrew recognized the bishop's face.

Andrew closed the gate behind him. Water ran from the gate's roof onto his shoulders.

He shivered.

Rain hissed through the trees.

Andrew walked into holly leaves. He strode quickly, feeling his way beside the box tombstone. Its chill lay wet under his fingers. He wondered if James would help. If he still existed.

Andrew hurried. His knuckles swung against a tree's bark. He sucked the pain away, and ran onto gravel.

The church windows glinted in front of him. The tower loomed, massively black.

Andrew turned, but he could see nothing in the darkness of the graveyard.

He stepped gently across the gravel towards the tower.

Perhaps the door was still open. He remembered Rosie not giving him time to shut it last night. Last night? Was it only a day since this terrible adventure began?

Andrew's hand found emptiness instead of the door's ancient timbers. He stepped in. His feet pushed deeply through the wet leaves. He crouched, feeling for the leaves, easing them out onto the gravel to allow the door to close. Rain trickled over his wrists. Then he gripped the door with both hands and firmly, but so slowly! quietly! began to edge it towards the door-frame.

Rain pattered.

Lightning whitened the church wall, the windows – for a moment – standing black and shining, then the thunder moaned, and Andrew pushed the door flat shut, hoping its sound would blend with the thunder.

He might have been blind.

His heart bumbled unpleasantly, muddling up his breathing. He rubbed rainwater from his brow.

Even now he was not really afraid. More curious. But questions he didn't like crept into his mind. Could the bishop find him by the noise he made?

Would a closed door keep him out?

Andrew knew the answer to that. The bishop had appeared in the kitchen, so neither doors nor walls nor fresh bright light could stop him.

But maybe – just maybe – he was like an ordinary person when he was searching; maybe he had to see Andrew to find him. Or hear him.

So Andrew stood still.

And waited.

He listened to the rain beyond the door.

He heard his own breath on his lips.

Water slid from his hair, down his neck. He snatched at his neck, and his clothes rustled.

White light flickered. He looked up as lightning danced, reaching down through a slit window, illuminating stone steps, lingering long enough for Andrew to turn again to the door; hoping, perhaps to find a bolt, or a key on the inside. Though he knew it was useless.

But as he turned, and the lightning shivered on the stone walls which rose so close all around, Andrew's jaws hauled themselves open; the ice of fear plunged onto his back and his hair stirred on his scalp.

Not two paces away, smiling, head dipping, stood the phantom of Bishop Redman.

Andrew fled up the stairs.

He heard screams bouncing off the walls. The screams stopped when he drew in a breath. Leaves slid from under his feet. His shins struck stony edges. He crawled up the spiralling stairway, darkness in his eyes, his brain silent with terror.

He fled upwards until his head struck something in the blackness, and he dropped, dazed, clutching the steps, grit under his fingers.

Andrew reached up. He felt wood and a handle.

He pushed, and fresh air bathed his face. The rain was off. He climbed onto the top of the church tower.

The walls of the tower menaced him, like the stone teeth of a giant, but with one tooth broken, fragments scattered around the tower floor, shattered by last night's lightning.

And the sky soared, yellow with the lights of the town.

Andrew dropped the trapdoor, and ran to the broken wall. He heard voices. Light poured freely – set free – from the vicarage windows. Beyond the vicarage, glowing among the trees in the front garden, was the blue swirl of a police car's lamp. And in the graveyard, torches bobbed towards the church.

Andrew's screams must have reached the house. He hauled in a breath to cry out.

"*Too late.*"

Andrew turned.

The old man beamed.

"*Too late, Andrew.*"

And it really was too late.

Andrew knew.

No one could arrive in time. Not now. And if they did, how could they help?

"*No, help, our Lord in ages past,*" smiled the bishop.

Andrew shrank against the wall. He clung to something cold on top of the wall. Something as broad as a school ruler, but buckled, where it had been blasted free of the stones.

The lightning conductor.

"*Time to go.*"

"No!"

"HURRY!" boomed from below.

"*Oh, yes.*"

The bishop stepped one pace closer. Then another.

One more and he would reach out...

Where is James now! snarled Andrew in his thoughts. Has he been teasing me? As usual!

The bishop's head wobbled nearer.

Andrew closed his eyes.

He felt something move beside him.

He opened his eyes. The bishop was hesitating.

Thoughts invaded Andrew's brain; thoughts that sparkled with intelligence and mocking humour.

And words formed inside his head, but not his own words.

"James?" he breathed.

Would I let you down, little brother?

The grin in the words tugged the muscles in Andrew's cheeks, forcing him to smile.

He uncoiled from the wall's embrace – turning his back on the conductor.

His own voice said, "Now, now, Bish, too late, as you say. Didn't take into account the Ainsley spirit, did you? Twist and tilt, old man, glaring won't do you a scrap of good. Want to meet my little brother? Fearless, he is. Well, pretty nearly. Good enough for you? Too good, I'm afraid. You can't have him. I've got him. I'm keeping him for myself. You're not the only one who wants to live on. Ha! Ha! Fooled you all, didn't I!

"You know someone who really, really! wants to

meet you again, Bish? Look behind you.

"Startling, isn't he? Just a heap of shadow with bright little eyes. All the better to see you with. I think he's inviting you home. Oh, dear, don't you want to go–o? What a shame! Well, I think you really, really! should, Bish. He's been waiting two hundred years to introduce you to his family. I believe he has a very big family –"

Lightning filled the sky.

Andrew glimpsed a shape in the shadows very clearly. He thought he heard a *clack* like small hoofs moving on the stone floor. He was fainting when someone plunged his back into boiling metal. That's what it felt like. Then that someone hit him a strange blow which seemed to strike inside and outside his body at the same time. An explosion filled the world. The sky turned above Andrew. Fragments of stone flew with him. He knew he had been flung across the tower. He hit the far wall without feeling it.

Then he dreamed of burning cloth. He dreamed of the smell of a million rotten eggs. He dreamed that his smile was his own – not James's – for everything was ended. The bishop was gone. He knew. And he himself was dying.

That didn't bother him. His only doubt was about James.

Then he stopped dreaming, and vanished from his own consciousness.

White walls.

And kind voices.

He knew he was Andrew Ainsley.

Hospital heat surrounded him. He discovered Rosie, red-eyed by his bed, and Mother and Father being brave.

Then he slept, with dreams.

Then he slept, later, drug-deep, without dreams.

He had told Father about running to the lychgate. About screaming up inside the tower.

He even spoke of the horror that had crouched in the dark at the top of the tower.

But he didn't mention James.

Andrew smiled as Rosie reported what the doctors had said: He should be dead. His wellingtons saved him, insulating him from the bolt of lightning which struck the conductor; burning his back and clothes. Luckily his jumper had been soaking, or the burns would have been worse. The blast had flung him across the tower, breaking a bone in his hand. Doctor John being in the tower was providential. And a good thing the police had thought to follow the doctor – eventually! in case they could help. They had radioed ahead to the hospital. Speed had saved Andrew's life.

His back would heal. His hand was no big problem.

Will I play the violin again?

But the doctors knew that old joke.

Sleep now. You can talk later.

Yes.

But he would never mention James.

He would never mention that James wanted to live on in Andrew's body. Then the lightning had blasted him away.

"But that wasn't greater love hath no man!"

cried Andrew. "If he had died selfishly, wouldn't the demon have got him?"

A hand rested, cool on his brow.

A voice floated, as if carried on the wind, with a breath of laughter in it.

Hush, now. No demons here. Sleep. Sleep sweetly, little brother.

Mocking silence.

Don't you know – it was all for you?

THE GARGOYLE

Hugh Scott

"No! No! No! You don't understand! The fear will kill you!"

On first sight, the new Scottish home of Professor Kent and his family seems quite idyllic. But there's a chill about the place that's not simply due to snow – an atmosphere of menace that young Marion, with her psychic powers, quickly senses. It seems to have something to do with the mysterious German and a boy called Callum who live in the nearby castle. Before long, Marion and her father find themselves in a tense battle of wits and wills – a life and death struggle that brings them face to face with the terrifying gargoyle...

"Followers of Hugh Scott will relish the mannered deliberation with which menace builds up in *The Gargoyle.*"
The Independent

"The kind of book that once you start you've got to finish. You can't possibly put it down for another sitting. It moves at a pretty cracking pace."
BBC Radio's Treasure Islands

A BOX OF TRICKS

Hugh Scott

"Simon Welkin! Come! We would converse with thee!"

Every summer, John and Maggie are packed off to stay with their Aunt Nell and Great-grandfather Harris in the country. But this year they get an explosive surprise, when Great-grandfather decides to waken the dead!

"Hugh Scott is at his best, stretching and exciting the imagination, producing glittering effects... Eerie and occasionally terrifying, beautifully evoking dark and light... The tension mounts to make the pulse race." *Susan Hill, The Sunday Times*

"Horror-hungry 10-year-olds will love it." *The Sunday Telegraph*

"A book which will be read time and again – a captivating ghost story which could well become a classic." *Time Out*

THE CAMERA OBSCURA

Hugh Scott

Spindletrim Tom's life at school is blighted by three bullies. His only refuge is Grandfather's antique shop, above which one day he discovers an amazing secret – a way of seeing into the past, present and future: the camera obscura. It's the start of some extraordinary events...

"The most intriguing and certainly the most excitingly written book I have read for a long time."
Mary Hoffman, The Sunday Telegraph

"Displays a Dahl-like exuberance and relish for the flesh and blood... An intriguing story." *School Librarian*

"It is full of fine lines and memorable images." *Jan Mark, The Times Educational Supplement*